COMMUNICATION IN TECHNOLOGY EDUCATION

EDITOR:

Jane A. Liedtke, Ph.D.
Associate Professor
Department of Industrial Technology
Illinois State University
Normal, Illinois 61761

39th Yearbook, 1990

Council on Technology Teacher Education

Glencoe/McGraw-Hill Publishing Company
15319 Chatsworth Street
P.O. Box 1509
Mission Hills, CA 91345-1509

Printed in the United States of America

**Orders and requests for information about cost and
availability of yearbooks should be addressed to the
company.**

Requests to quote portions of yearbooks should be addressed to the
Secretary, Council on Technology Education, in care of the
publisher, for forwarding to the current Secretary.

**This publication
is available in microform.**

University Microfilms International

300 North Zeeb Road
Dept. P.R.
Ann Arbor, MI 48106

ISBN 0-02-677116-0

Foreword

Technology teacher education is facing exciting and challenging times. No area is more important than redirecting curriculum to reflect contemporary technology education. This yearbook is the first, in what is hoped to be, a series that explores the Jackson's Mills curriculum organizers: communication, construction, manufacturing, and transportation.

The editor and chapter authors took on the challenge of viewing communication from a new vantage point. Their proposal stated, "In technology education it is no longer appropriate to approach curriculum as segregated content areas such as graphic communications, graphic arts, electronics, or even computer applications. Present and future communications depend heavily on fully integrated systems . . ." With this perspective, the team set out to develop a yearbook that would provide an orientation to communication technology and com-munication systems applicable to learning experiences at all levels of technology education.

The first three chapters provide a background by presenting the concept, history, and application of communication technology. The next three chapters present conceptual models for public school and university communication programs. The next three address activities, learning environments and evaluation techniques for teaching communication. The final chapter synthesizes the entire book.

This yearbook promises to be a valuable resource for each technology educator. We all owe the editor and the several authors our appreciation. The best way to do this is read the yearbook, communicate with the authors, and apply the ideas that are appropriate to our situation.

April, 1990   R. Thomas Wright
                                               President, CTTE

Yearbook Planning Committee

Terms Expiring in 1990

William E. Dugger
Virginia Polytechnic Institute and State University

Jack Kirby
University of Wisconsin-Platteville

Terms Expiring in 1991

Donald Lauda
California State University-Long Beach

John R. Wright
Central Connecticut State University

Terms Expiring in 1992

Donald Maley
University of Maryland

Ronald E. Jones
University of North Texas

Terms Expiring in 1993

Paul W. DeVore
West Virginia University

Everett Israel
Eastern Michigan University

Terms Expiring in 1994

Anthony Schwaller
St. Cloud State University

Robert Wenig
North Carolina State University

Chairperson

R. Thomas Wright
Ball State University

Officers of the Council

President

R. Thomas Wright
Department of Industry and Technology
Ball State University
Muncie, IN 47306

Vice-President

Jane A. Liedtke
Department of Industrial Technology
Illinois State University
Normal, IL 61761

Membership Secretary

Gerald L. Jennings
Department of Business and Industrial Education
Eastern Michigan University
Ypsilanti, MI 48197

Recording Secretary

James E. LaPorte
Technology Education Program
Virginia Polytechnic Institute and State University
Blacksburg, VA 24061

Treasurer

A. Emerson Wiens
Department of Industrial Technology
Illinois State University
Normal, IL 61761

Yearbook Proposals

Each year, at the ITEA International conference, the CTTE Yearbook Committee reviews the progress of yearbooks in preparation and evaluates proposals for additional yearbooks. Any member is welcome to submit a yearbook proposal. It should be written in sufficient detail for the committee to be able to understand the proposed substance and format. Fifteen copies of the proposal should be sent to the committee chairperson by February 1 of the year in which the conference is held. Below are the criteria employed by the committee in making yearbook selections.

CTTE Yearbook Committee

CTTE Yearbook Guidelines

A. Purpose:
The CTTE Yearbook Series is intended as a vehicle for communicating education subject matter in a structured, formal series that does not duplicate commercial textbook publishing activities.

B. Yearbook topic selection criteria:
An appropriate Yearbook topic should:
1. Make a direct contribution to the understanding and improvement of technology teacher education.
2. Add to the accumulated body of knowledge of the field.
3. Not duplicate publishing activities of commercial publishers or other professional groups.
4. Provide a balanced view of the theme and not promote a single individual's or institution's philosophy or practices.
5. Actively seek to upgrade and modernize professional practice in technology teacher education.
6. Lend itself to team authorship as opposed to single authorship.

Proper yearbook themes *may* also be structured to:
1. Discuss and critique points of view which have gained a degree of acceptance by the profession.
2. Raise controversial questions in an effort to obtain a national hearing.
3. Consider and evaluate a variety of seemingly conflicting trends and statements emanating from several sources.

C. The yearbook proposal:
1. The Yearbook Proposal should provide adequate detail for the Yearbook Planning Committee to evaluate its merits.
2. The Yearbook Proposal should include:
   (a) An introduction to the topic
   (b) A listing of chapter titles
   (c) A brief description of the content or purpose of each chapter
   (d) A tentative list of authors for the various chapters
   (e) An estimate of the length of each chapter

Previously Published
Yearbooks

*1. *Inventory Analysis of Industrial Arts Teacher Education Facilities, Personnel and Programs*, 1952.

*2. *Who's Who in Industrial Arts Teacher Education*, 1953.

*3. *Some Components of Current Leadership: Techniques of Selection and Guidance of Graduate Students; An Analysis of Textbook Emphases*; 1954, three studies.

*4. *Superior Practices in Industrial Arts Teacher Education*, 1955.

*5. *Problems and Issues in Industrial Arts Teacher Education*, 1956.

*6. *A Sourcebook of Reading in Education for Use in Industrial Arts and Industrial Arts Teacher Education*, 1957.

*7. *The Accreditation of Industrial Arts Teacher Education*, 1958.

*8. *Planning Industrial Arts Facilities*, 1959. Ralph K. Nair, ed.

*9. *Research in Industrial Arts Education*, 1960. Raymond Van Tassel, ed.

*10. *Graduate Study in Industrial Arts*, 1961. R. P. Norman and R. C. Bohn, eds.

*11. *Essentials of Preservice Preparation*, 1962. Donald G. Lux, ed.

*12. *Action and Thought in Industrial Arts Education*, 1963. E. A. T. Svendsen, ed.

*13. *Classroom Research in Industrial Arts*, 1964.Charles B. Porter, ed.

*14. *Approaches and Procedures in Industrial Arts*, 1965. G. S. Wall, ed.

*15. *Status of Research in Industrial Arts*, 1966. John D. Rowlett, ed.

*16. *Evaluation Guidelines for Contemporary Industrial Arts Programs*, 1967. Lloyd P. Nelson and William T. Sargent, eds.

*17. *A Historical Perspective of Industry*, 1968. Joseph F. Luetkemeyer, Jr., ed.

*18. *Industrial Technology Education*, 1969. C. Thomas Dean and N.A. Hauer, eds. *Who's Who in Industrial Arts Teacher Education*, 1969. John M. Pollock and Charles A. Bunten, eds.

*19. *Industrial Arts for Disadvantaged Youth*, 1970. Ralph O. Gallington, ed.

*20. *Components of Teacher Education*, 1971. W. E. Ray and J. Streichler, eds.

*21. *Industrial Arts for the Early Adolescent*, 1972. Daniel L. Householder, ed.

*22. *Industrial Arts in Senior High Schools*, 1973. Rutherford E. Lockette, ed.

*23. *Industrial Arts for the Elementary School*, 1974. Robert G. Thrower and Robert D. Weber, eds.

*24. *A Guide to the Planning of Industrial Arts Facilities*, 1975. D. E. Moon, ed.

*25. *Future Alternatives for Industrial Arts*, 1976. Lee H. Smalley, ed.

*26. *Competency-Based Industrial Arts Teacher Education*, 1977. Jack C. Brueckman and Stanley E. Brooks, eds.

*27. *Industrial Arts in the Open Access Curriculum*, 1978. L. D. Anderson, ed.

*28. *Industrial Arts Education: Retrospect, Prospect*, 1979. G. Eugene Martin, ed.

*29. *Technology and Society: Interfaces with Industrial Arts*, 1980. Herbert A. Anderson and M. James Benson, eds.

*30. *An Interpretive History of Industrial Arts*, 1981. Richard Barella and Thomas Wright, eds.

*31. *The Contributions of Industrial Arts to Selected Areas of Education*, 1982. Donald Maley and Kendall N. Starkweather, eds.

*32. *The Dynamics of Creative Leadership for Industrial Arts Education*, 1983. Robert E. Wenig and John I. Mathews, eds.

*33. *Affective Learning in Industrial Arts*, 1984. Gerald L. Jennings, ed.

*34. *Perceptual and Psychomotor Learning in Industrial Arts Education*, 1985. John M. Shemick, ed.

*35. *Implementing Technology Education*, 1986. Ronald E. Jones and John R. Wright, eds.

*36. *Conducting Technical Research*, 1987. Everett N. Israel and R. Thomas Wright, eds.

*37. *Instructional Strategies for Technology Education*, 1988. William H. Kemp and Anthony E. Schweller, eds.

*38. *Technology Student Organizations*, 1989. M. Roger Betts and Arvid W. VanDyke, eds.

---

*Out-of-print yearbooks can be obtained in microfilm and in Xerox copies. For information on price and delivery, write to Xerox University Microfilms, 300 North Zeeb Road, Ann Arbor, Michigan, 48106.

Contents

Chapter 1

Communication Technology 1

Sharon A. Brusic
  Virginia Polytechnic Institute and State University

Chapter 2

Communication Systems in Business, Industry, and Government 20

Frank Trocki
  Northeastern University

Chapter 3

History of Communication Content in Technology Education 38

Janet L. Robb and Ronald E. Jones
  University of North Texas

Chapter 4

Conceptual Models for Communication in Technology Education Programs at the Elementary, Middle School, and Junior High School Levels 50

Donna K. Trautman
  Bowling Green University

Chapter 5

Conceptual Models for Communication in Technology Education Programs at the High School Level 62

Richard D. Seymour
  Ball State University

Preface

We live in the "Information Age" where the means of
communication has rapidly advanced the process of sending,
receiving, and storing messages. In technology education it is no
longer appropriate to approach curriculum as segregated content
areas such as graphic communications, graphic arts, drafting,
electronics, or even computer applications. Present and future
communication depends heavily on fully integrated systems which
network a variety of components with impressive capabilities. This
CTTE yearbook provides an orientation to communication
technology and communication systems applicable to learning
experiences at all levels of technology education.

The first two chapters (Chapters 1 and 2) are an introduction to
communication technology and communication systems. The
function of communication technology in our global environment
and the impact it has on society is presented. Communication
models from business, industry, and the government contribute to
the understanding of rapid technological changes in communication
technology within these sectors of our society.

The next four chapters (Chapters 3, 4, 5, and 6) provide the
rationale for exploring communication in technology education and
support the development of programs and content selection.
Historical perspectives as well as contemporary approaches support
the philosophical and curricular basis for the study of
communication in technology education. Models for the study of
communication at the elementary, middle school, junior high and
high school levels and in technology teacher education programs
are given. These models provide the scope and sequence of content
appropriate for technology education at each level. Such models
provide the structure and direction for the classroom teacher and
those preparing to teach communication content at that level.

Three subsequent chapters (Chapters 7, 8, and 9) present
methods for determining and developing communication activities
and strategies for obtaining teaching materials to support activities.
Considerations for establishing the communication teaching and
learning environment including planning facilities for the
curriculum and support developmental strategies for flexible
environments where creative problem solving and positive
classroom/laboratory experiences with advancing technology can
occur. Methods for evaluating and improving teaching and learning

about communication technology and systems are given with
reference to the Standards for Technology
Education Programs. This includes the characteristics of quality
communication programs within technology education.

The final chapter (Chapter 10) is a summary and synthesis of the
major trends and issues identified throughout the yearbook.
Direction and guidance for individuals implementing
communication in technology education programs is included. It is
the intent that this yearbook will facilitate and encourage a level of
change in technology education programs that will rival the rapid
technological growth and advancement which now occurs
throughout business and industry.

Acknowledgments

The editor wishes to express thanks and sincere appreciation to those who contributed to this project. Publications such as a yearbook require the cooperative efforts of many individuals. The chapter
authors and co-authors who gave of their time and talents deserve special recognition. These dedicated professionals made the 39th Yearbook possible. Many thanks to each author for meeting short deadlines and great expectations! It has been a pleasure working with each of you.

A special thanks to Wes Stephens for help in editing the yearbook manuscript. Wes' wisdom and expertise were valuable assistance. In addition, I am grateful to Julie Amdor, Cindy Dick, and Pam Hawkins for contributing to the computer entry and processing of the manuscript.

My friends and colleagues are appreciated for their support, sympathy, and encouragement throughout the two years of the project.
Finally, the Glencoe Publishing Company is gratefully acknowledged for their support of the Council on Technology Teacher Education and their assistance throughout this yearbook project.

Jane A. Liedtke

Chapter 1

COMMUNICATION TECHNOLOGY

Sharon A. Brusic
Research Associate
Technology Education Program Area
Virginia Polytechnic Institute and State University
Blacksburg, Virginia

Perspectives on Communication Technology

Human endeavors to perfect communication systems and facilitate the exchange of information and ideas are constantly challenged in a technological society. Even supercomputers and high-speed photonics have not suppressed the researcher's desire to improve techniques for sending and receiving information. New technologies spur new problems which are solved with improved machines and systems that make communication more efficient, expedient, economical, and effective. Furthermore, as these new technologies are interjected into the social system that makes them useful, more changes evolve and new problems and applications are realized, thus eliciting more inventions and innovations. In effect, communication technology exemplifies the notion that change begets change.

The Changing Picture in Communication

It comes as no revelation to say that communication devices prevalent in the last quarter of the twentieth century are far different from those that made information transfer possible at the turn of the century. Likewise, the technical means employed to transmit information in the next century will invariably differ from those methods in use today. Humans expect communication systems to change, even improve, over time. Progress is frequently associated with better communication and systems that make tasks easier, faster, and more reliable.

1

Historically, the evolution of human-based communication techniques has been chronologically arranged from some point in the Stone Age (approximately 20,000 B.C.), through the use of cave drawings and hieroglyphics, to the present (1990's), labeled the Information Age, distinguished by artificial intelligence systems, fiber optics, telecommunications, and high-speed facsimile transmission. In general, every other communication technique that exists at present, or has existed in the past, can be found somewhere between these two points.

Impetus for
Communication Technology Developments

Human nature and the desire to respond to human needs are largely responsible for the pace of technological development that exists for communication systems. The human need for self-preservation directly affected advancements in long-distance communication during prehistoric times. Primitive people used signals, including gestures, fires, and drums, to communicate with others about the presence of food or to warn them of imminent danger.

The desire to send complex messages over long distances gave impetus to developments in telecommunication, most notably through the use of electromagnetism in telegraphy and telephony. National defense needs during wartime were the catalyst for developing radio direction and ranging, more commonly known as radar. More recently, in response to human demands for better resolution on television screens, high definition television (HDTV) emerged.

Each technological development is generally the result of a combination of social, economic, environmental, and political factors that stimulate invention and innovation. Seldom do communication technologies surface without some of these stimuli. Initially, these new technologies may not realize their full potential or total market. In some cases, it takes decades before a communication technology becomes economically feasible or socially accepted. Facsimile transmission is an excellent example of a communication technology with a delayed impact. Despite decades of extensive use in publishing industries for transmitting photographs, facsimile only recently made an impact on business and domestic communications. In fact, facsimile transmission threatened overnight express companies' markets by making immediate transmission of printed information economically feasible for a large number of organizations.

Trends in Communication Technology

Considerable evidence suggests concurrent innovations in electronics and computer technology will continue to have great effect on communication systems. A 1985 study by the Office of Technology Assessment (OTA) credits microelectronics and software development for the rapid pace of technological improvement in communications industries. Without question, present trends suggest that computerization is a key factor in nearly all modern communication technologies.

An examination of the present state of communication technology leads one to recognize possible futures. It is always risky, however, to "predict" the direction of a particular technology based on existing practices. In order to circumvent this problem, projections are made in terms of general presages: transmission systems, integrated networks, standardization, information storage, personal systems, and regulation.

Transmission Systems. By and large, the transmission systems in place to transport voice, data, and images are the critical components of effective, efficient communication. Technology has progressed steadily in this area and shows every indication of further development. In addition to expanded use of fiber optics, microwaves, lasers, satellites, and cables, new innovations are expected that make these technologies more accurate and economical. Transmission systems will carry more information over greater distances with greater speed; hence making information transfer more expedient and timely.

Integrated Networks. Networking voice (or sound), data, and images through integrated systems is clearly a prevailing trend. The use of sophisticated computer systems linked with high-volume, adaptable transmission systems makes it feasible to converge technologies and facilitate access to a multitude of systems and data bases. This trend is exemplified in a number of businesses and industries that rely on services and systems, such as electronic mail, computerized inventory control, teleconferencing, and data base access and management.

As integrated networks mature, consumer applications are certain to improve. Rowan A. Wakefield (1986), editor of a national newsletter on family policy and programs, predicts that information technology, especially the home computer and expert systems, will empower families by giving them more control over leisure time, education, health care, government, and related professional service needs (i.e., financial, travel, legal).

Standardization. For decades, industries and consumers have recognized the problems of incompatibility. Whether working with computers, video tape recorders, or video disks, the problem is equally distressing. Efforts to standardize communication systems is ongoing, and current trends suggest that developments are underway to conform communications protocol; thus enabling connections between diverse systems. Today, there is considerable lack of common standards among manufacturers, which confounds networking problems and severely limits users' flexibility. There is evidence of progress towards standardization that should greatly enhance communication systems and foster new applications of existing technologies.

Information Storage. Presently, the industry is moving toward optical storage systems that store vast amounts of analog and digital information and provide ready access to data. Unfortunately, optical storage has limited recording capabilities for the typical consumer. Present-day applications are most useful for accessing information from professionally produced and marketed disks. For example, optical storage systems are extremely useful in library settings, whereby computers can access information from compact disks that store complete volumes of encyclopedias or research abstracts. It is reasonable to expect this market to expand greatly to include an increased selection of optical storage systems and improved accessibility and recording options.

Personal Systems. Expansion of personal systems is directly related to growth in other areas of communication technology, namely transmission systems, standardization, and integrated networks. In general, a clear emphasis is on technology that is geared toward the consumer and the home market. It is expected that consumer sales in home computer systems, software packages, and telecommunications devices or services will continue to escalate. According to the United States Department of Commerce (1988), 48.7% of American households contained a video cassette recorder in 1987, compared with only 1.1% in 1980. Furthermore, cable television subscriptions have risen from 19.8% in 1980 to 48.7% in 1987.

As the technology becomes available at a reasonable cost, increasing numbers of consumers are expected to buy into the

4

"Information Age." Electronic media sales, especially in cellular phones and home computer systems tied into electronic bulletin boards, will expectedly rise.

Regulations. The landmark breakup of American Telephone and Telegraph (AT&T) during the 1980's set a precedent in the telecommunications industry that is certain to have ramifications for years to come. Deregulation appears to be a growing trend throughout government and will probably continue through the next several decades. The policies established could greatly affect the expedient growth of the communications industries and influence the environment for implementing competitive information systems.

Looking Into The Future:
The Impact of Communication Systems

New technologies have the potential to affect significantly the human capabilities for transmitting and receiving information. As evidenced throughout history, humans have consistently strived to invent and innovate communication systems. Whether communication systems are used to transmit sounds, images or data, they have shown steady technical improvement over the past several centuries, and there is no indication that progress may be halted.

Accessibility of Information. As people become more comfortable with information technology, it is reasonable to expect that communication networks will expand to include services and information that appeal to every sector of the population. An integrated network of data banks, personal computers, and facsimile systems has the potential to make vast amounts of information accessible in every home, school, and office at a reasonable cost. Present trends in this direction suggest that public access to information should be more attainable.

Edward Wenk, Jr., former science and technology advisor to Congress and science policy staff member to Presidents Kennedy, Johnson, and Nixon, enumerates several recommendations to address the information access problem in the United States. In his book *Tradeoffs*, Wenk (1986) advises that the Library of Congress function as the hub for national communication networks based in public libraries. Furthermore, he suggests that the Federal Communications Commission require cable networks to dedicate interactive communication channels as a public service commitment. Regardless of whether these ideas materialize in the future, it is evident that technology makes information access potentially more feasible and undeniably less tedious.

Quality of Communications. Improved quality of communication systems is a goal of most technological research and development. The quality of the communication system is generally enhanced through efficient and economic use of resources in developing the product or maintaining the system. Through research and development, especially in microelectronics and photonics, the quality of communication systems is certain to improve.

Another factor in quality communications concerns the nature of the communication system itself. As more and better channels of communication become available, the quality of the communication network should be enhanced. In the future, new channels of communication are projected that will make communication systems easier to use, more portable, more reliable, and less costly.

Industry's proclaimed commitment to planning and development in the area of high definition television (HDTV) is one example of the impact of better quality communication systems. Presumably, HDTV will have a pronounced impact on the quality of electronic, visual communication devices.

The Human Factor. The increased use of computers and automated information systems is, however, not without its negative consequences. Consumers, social and political activists, and environmentalists are voicing opposition to the prevailing technology craze. They raise valid criticisms of a "technology driven society." It is not uncommon to hear media reports of communication technology devices used to exploit people, promote injustice in the workplace, manipulate records, or seize personal privacy. Some people question the benefit of these technologies for the average citizen, while others point out that expanded information networks exacerbate problems for those people and institutions that can ill-afford to participate in the system. Can greater expense for new communication technology be justified when nearly one-third of the American population is illiterate? (Hirsch, 1988).

Although personal systems look promising in terms of their availability, some people question the readiness of the public. Do consumers need and want home-based information networks available only to the economically privileged? Will society truly benefit from, and effectively use, this technology? In his book *The World Wired Up,*

Brian Murphy (1983) provides a graphic description of this dilemma:
. . . we are told that if we don't 'cable up', 'digitalise',or get a
'bird' in the sky as soon as possible, our society will be left
behind in the dust of history. The public must choose
quickly, with its cash or with its vote. And once these
technologies are there, we are told, there will be an increase in democracy (as more people have access to the
government via interactive television), society will be better managed, resources will be more equally apportioned,
and leisure time will become more fulfilling. (p. 11)

On the positive side, technological developments make a significant
contribution to communication capabilities and enable humans to
share information instantaneously around the globe. Improved techniques that provide for efficient exchange of sound, data, and images
are essential components of successful twentieth-century enterprises.
As new technology becomes embedded in the economic, political, and
social framework, people adapt and benefit from the new capacities it
affords. Among other things, communication technology can strength-
en human relationships (telephone contacts), improve understanding
(educational television), facilitate tasks (computer applications), and
promote informed citizenship (newspaper and radio).

What is Communication Technology?

The perspective presented to this point demonstrates that communication technology is ubiquitous. Not only has it pervaded history,
but also methods and systems for proliferating human capabilities to
communicate are indispensable resources for the future.

At this point, however, it is helpful to pause and further contemplate what is meant by communication technology. In the next section, communication technology is described through three means:
definition of the terms, inspection of a communication process model,
and depiction of the systematic nature of communication. Then, the
linkages made possible through communication technology are explored through a cursory review of social, political, scientific, industrial, and environmental implications.

Defining Communication Technology. Rather than providing a
definitive explanation of communication technology at the onset, it is
useful to examine the terms, communication and technology, sep-
arately. Then, perhaps, a more complete understanding of their collective meaning is realized.

7

Technology is generally the most difficult of the two words to describe. Definitions of this term range from the concrete (depictions of technology as tools, machines, and product) to the abstract (characterizations of technology as "know-how" or cognition). Technology is unquestionably a complex concept which means different things to each person.

In an effort to clarify the subject, however, technology is henceforth described through four themes, as delineated by Mitcham (1980) and Frey (1987): technology as objects, (or artifacts), process (making and using), knowledge, and volition. By describing technology as such, it is evident that technology includes not only the material objects that it uses or makes available, but it also takes into consideration those processes or techniques that facilitate the production of these goods, the knowledge necessary to solve the problems and extend human capabilities, and the choices and decisions (volition) that are necessarily involved with technology. Technology, thus portrayed, embraces a variety of attributes.

When the term, communication, is combined with technology, its meaning becomes more explicit. Communication technology refers to the tools, techniques, knowledge, choices, and decisions associated with sending and receiving information. This information, or data, exchange serves one or more purposes, to: inform, educate, persuade, entertain, or control. Accordingly, telephones, printing processes, understanding of fiber optic transmission, and television viewers' choices are each considered components of communication technology.

To further explicate communication technology, it is useful to inspect models that depict the communication process and its inherent system.

The Communication Process. Communication is frequently portrayed through a model first introduced by Shannon and Weaver (1949). Figure 1.1 illustrates this communication process by including the following components: information source, message encoding, transmitter, receiver, message decoding, destination, and noise source.

The information source refers to the message originator. In most cases, the information source is the human brain; however, there are other information sources which are "intelligent" machines. The component or feature that generates commands acts as the information source.

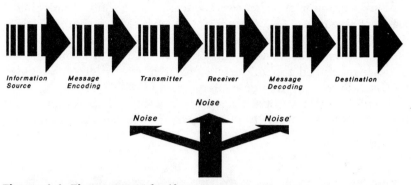

Information   Message   Transmitter   Receiver   Message   Destination
Source   Encoding   Decoding

Noise

Noise   Noise

Figure 1.1: The communication process.

In order to transmit a message, it is necessary to encode it. Encoding refers to the process of changing the message into a form that is readily transmittable via the selected channel. For example, if a vocal message is transmitted using a telephone, it is encoded by converting sounds into electrical or optical impulses. These impulses are conveyed through the transmitter, or communication channel.

Technological apparatuses act as transmitters in the communication process and include such devices as televisions, satellites, radios, books, facsimile machines, and computers. It is not uncommon to involve several transmitters in a typical communication process, as when television programs are aired through a combination of antenna, cables, satellites, and relay stations.

Once the message is transmitted, the communication process becomes complete once the signal is received and decoded at its destination. This means that the transmitted message is accepted, the signals are changed back into a comprehensible form, and the message is processed by the destination. In this case, the destination is similar to the information source, except that it is the message receiver rather than the message initiator.

In addition, the communication process typically includes some type of interference, referred to as the noise source in the Shannon and Weaver model. Any distraction in the communication system, regardless of where in the process it occurs, is called noise. Any number of noise sources exist in a standard communication system. Electric current oscillations, excess background clamor, fluctuations in the light source, and faulty wiring are factors that could severely affect the message transfer. Noise sources must be considered in any communication system and should be eliminated or diminished as much as possible.

Many communication process models include a final component, feedback (see Figure 1.2). Once the message is received at the destination, there is often a return message, or response. Even in the case of machine communications, feedback is relevant. For example, if a message instructed a robotic arm device to move, the device provides feedback to the information source indicating that the message was received. In effect, feedback is the feature of the process that causes the process to repeat itself until all message transfers are complete.

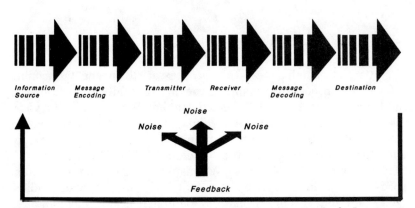

Figure 1.2: Communication process models often include feedback.

A thorough understanding of the communication process helps clarify the meaning of communication by breaking it down into its component parts. Furthermore, when communication is assessed according to its relationship with technology, the process approach fosters a clear, detailed analysis of each step involved in message transmission. This is critical in communication technology when technical means are employed to improve the process of transmitting and receiving messages.

The Communication System. Though the process approach to evaluating communication technology is valid, it does not clearly articulate one important feature of communications: the interdependent nature of each component part. General systems theorists argue that communication is a system. Lewis Thomas (1979) explains that:

> A system is a structure of interacting, intercommunicating components that, as a group, act or operate individually and jointly to achieve a common goal through the concerted activity of the individual parts. (p. 15)

The communication system is depicted in Figure 1.3 and includes four basic components: inputs, processes, outputs, and impacts. Inputs include those resources that are necessary to process the message and include seven elements: people, information, materials, tools and machines, energy, capital, and time. Processes in the communication system include all those procedures used to convey the message to the receiver, and outputs are described as the received messages.

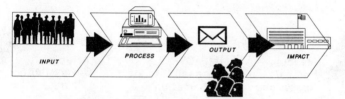

Figure 1.3: Four basic components comprise a communication system.

Additionally, all communication systems have incidental and intentional impacts which directly affect the inputs, processes, and outputs of the system. These impacts take place in the context of larger systems where they consequently influence a host of other factors. To illustrate this, see Figure 1.4. In this example, it is clearly demonstrated that a typical communication system can significantly affect related social, environmental, political, economic, and industrial systems.

The systems approach to communication makes it possible to designate each component (i.e., input, process, output, and impact) as a critical system element. If any component is defective, deficient, or unsatisfactory, it not only causes communication inadequacies, but it also potentially influences a multitude of other systems and constituencies.

In effect, the systems approach focuses attention on the interconnectedness of inputs, processes, outputs, and impacts, and it forces recognition of the link that exists between components and systems. In communication technology, this is essential if the goal is to furnish efficient, expedient, economical, and effective transmissions of voice, images, and data.

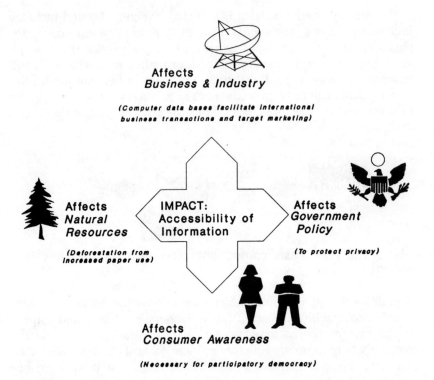

Figure 1.4: Communication systems impact larger interrelated systems.

Communication: An Essential Technological Link

It is imperative that communication technology be recognized as an essential link in a technological society. As Wenk (1986) states:

> It [technology] is itself a social system driven by specialized knowledge and involving all the institutions of our society and their communication linkages. As a social process, technology deals with people, with their values, with political choice in democratic governance, and with connections between all three. (p. 3)

In effect, multifarious communication systems serve a vital function in a technological society by facilitating efficient information exchange between people, organizations, and institutions. However, when communication linkages permeate society, they yield detriments, as well as benefits. As new technologies evolve, their assets and liabilities surface, sometimes revealing unexpected or unintended results. The social, political, scientific, industrial, and environmental implications of modern communication systems constitute a type of technological "fallout" that must be addressed in a democratic community.

Social Implications. The invention and innovation of a vast number of communication technologies constantly alters methods used to send and receive messages. As a result, there are a number of avenues available for people to transmit their ideas, images, and thoughts. The accessibility of communication devices in homes, businesses, and public arenas makes it conceivable for almost any person to communicate with another person anywhere on the globe, instantaneously. The "global neighborhood" manifests itself through the expansion of communication systems that make immediate communication a reality.

The advantage of instantaneous communications is evidenced in its contribution to building and maintaining personal and professional human relationships. New communication techniques foster opportunities for international relations and connections by minimizing distances and simplifying contacts.

However, communication technologies sometimes reap apparently negative consequences. The U. S. Department of Commerce (1987) reports that the average American views 7.2 hours of television per day. This startling figure, which has risen steadily since 1950, indicates that people spend nearly one-third of their lives as passive recipients of broadcast media. Moreover, quality programming is highly elusive; biased news reporting, melodramatic "soap operas," and violent or aggressive shows capture audiences' attention and possibly detract from the educational benefits of the medium.

In the meantime, educational reports indicate that students graduate from schools unprepared to live and work in a technologically advanced society (National Science Board, 1983). Though educational applications of communication technologies are available to alleviate some of this problem, federal support is highly inadequate to support such an undertaking. In 1982, the Office of Technology Assessment proposed several options to Congress as a response to technological deficiencies in schools. Of greatest interest in this report was the emphasis placed on research, development, and acquisition of state-of-the-art communication technologies, including satellite communications, computer networking, electronic conferencing, and information data base systems. There is a striking contrast gap between the proliferation of technology in society as a whole and the educational community specifically. Unless the social system adapts and implements new technologies successfully, technological illiteracy is bound to remain high and is certain to affect the United States' competitiveness internationally.

Privacy issues have prevailed throughout the current communications revolution and are certain to solicit greater attention in the years to come. Oscar H. Gandy, a professor of communication arts and sciences, and Charles E. Simmons, a journalism instructor, both of Harvard University, argue that:

> . . . the promise of information technology and the 'television of abundance' brings not the emancipations of diversity, access and participation, but an accelerated disintegration of an already weakened right to privacy at the same time that it threatens the very foundations of participatory democracy. (Gandy & Simmons, 1986, p. 155)

Gandy and Simmons (1986) assert that sophisticated communication systems enable the wealthy and powerful to manipulate unknowing citizens. Through complex information networks that feasibly access vast amounts of data about personal and private characteristics and choices, certain groups or individuals have benefited greatly. Of greatest concern is the application of these technologies to consumer marketing and political lobbying. In both of these instances, personal privacy is at stake through the legal exploitation of communication technology.

Advanced communication devices have the potential to mobilize information and ideas, just as transportation systems have mobilized people for centuries. However, if abused or applied in such ways as to oppress people or diminish personal rights, the democratic society is threatened.

Political Implications. The political ramifications of advanced communication systems are, without doubt, a highly controversial issue. Though not always explicitly stated as such, communication technology is largely responsible for the sophistication of national intelligence and defense systems. Nearly eighty percent of direct government funding for research and development in information technology is supplied by the Department of Defense (OTA, 1985). The predominance of military support in this area signifies the importance of communication systems for supplying timely information and ensuring expedient, accurate transfer of data, images, and information.

Surveillance systems, on the other hand, collect and sort information from a number of sources. They hold the potential for the abuse or possible contemptuous use of technology for collaborating information about people and organizations. Though oftentimes associated with conspiracy, surveillance systems serve a beneficial purpose when used to protect the welfare of people and nations.

In an effort to promote global competitiveness and maintain national security, a healthy economic climate is vital. In today's society, information technology is often the key to economic prosperity. Some people claim that information-rich organizations directly correlate with economic wealth. The ability to access, handle, and employ information is requisite for a nation to maintain its competitive edge and financial security.

However, political implications of communication technology are not always as abstract as economics and national intelligence. The abundance of information, and available systems for filtering and organizing the information, have given politicians a remarkable new tool for accomplishing their goals. Communication systems maximize the impact of political messages and have the potential to increase the efficiency of targeting supporters in both the public and private sector. Direct mail campaigns aimed at specific populations (i.e., small businesspersons, blacks, elected officials, women, elderly, etc.) can solicit considerable support for legislative issues and play a key role in influencing voters and decision makers. Modern technology makes it possible for lobbyists to target individuals with "personalized" letters that relate to their viewpoints and values (by accessing officials' voting records and census data, for example). By using computers and laser printers that output over 7,000 letters per minute, politicians find it is possible to mass communicate using ostensibly personal communications. Gandy and Simmons describe cases that optimize this technique when targeting citizens and, in the process, exclude certain groups (i.e., gay populations, or certain races). ". . . We see even at this somewhat primitive stage in the development of targeted propaganda campaigns, true participatory democracy is gravely threatened" (Gandy & Simmons, 1986, p. 162).

Scientific and Industrial Implications. Communication technology is, likewise, a key factor in scientific and industrial endeavors, most notably in the area of research and development. Throughout history, documentation of information and dissemination of new knowledge has been fundamental to technical progress. Communication systems facilitate information exchange around the globe and make it possible for researchers to store and access vast amounts of information. The expanded knowledge base presents scientists and technologists with a vast pool of information essential to invention and innovation. The competitive environment surrounding scientific and technological research and development is strengthened by communication systems that extend human potential and enhance abilities to collect, store, synthesize, and analyze information which results in greater personal and professional rewards.

Corporations utilize communication techniques to link researchers and engineers. Advanced computer-aided design systems simplify production operations from ideation through manufacturing. And, better communication systems improve scientific research through improved accuracy of monitoring devices, imaging techniques, and data transmission networks. Space probes and satellites provide scientists with essential data for understanding the universe and predicting environmental trends.

Though scientific and industrial implications of communication developments appear to be mostly positive on the surface, negative implications exist. For example, unsolicited facsimile messages, oftentimes called "junk fax," cause considerable delay in transmitting legitimate messages, resulting in unwarranted queing and escalating paper costs. Efforts are already underway in some states to establish strict guidelines for facsimile transmission in an effort to alleviate this problem. Furthermore, electronic transmission of information unknowingly or accidentally intercepted by others raises ethical questions, especially in government or proprietary business transactions.

Expanded information networks and more powerful communication systems undoubtedly generate new challenges and opportunities for science and industry. At the same time, however, it becomes necessary to question the legitimacy of these applications to assure all people of fair and ethical treatment.

Environmental Implications. Technological development is often portrayed as an asset to any given culture. The synonymity of technology and progress is vehemently negated when one considers potential environmental implications of communication technology. Technological "progress" is largely responsible for the destruction of millions of acres of forests as paper and paper products proliferate. Edward Tenner, executive editor at Princeton University Press, explains that America's paper consumption increased 320% from 1959 to 1986, and he predicts that increased electronic communications will only accelerate the pace. He writes:

> The paperless office, the leafless library, the inkless newspaper, the cashless, checkless society -- all have gone the way of the Empire State Building's dirigible mooring, the backyard helipad, the nuclear-powered convertible, the vitamin-pill dinner and the Paperwork Reduction Act of 1980. The micro-millennium is turning out to be the cellulose century. (Tenner, 1988, p. 53)

The ramifications of increased paper use far exceed deforestation concerns. Though paper products are generally recyclable, many communities are ill-equipped to handle such disposal arrangements, and typical consumers don't want to sort trash. As a result, waste disposal is a grave concern that is exacerbated by increased paper consumption. Furthermore, there are direct and indirect effects on wildlife, waterways, and air quality as natural resources are tapped for increased paper production and printing.

Environmental implications of communication technology surface in other ways. Electronic devices and computers cause noise pollution (the electronic hum in offices); earth stations, antennas, and neon signage destroy community aesthetics; and, increased atmospheric microwave transmissions cause some to question the long-term impact on natural systems.

Additionally, communication technology can improve environmental conditions. The use of computer graphics enables architects and developers to improve urban and regional planning ventures through advance analysis. New transmission systems minimize above-ground cables and contribute to improving environmental images. Weather satellites make it possible to track storms, prepare for adverse conditions, and reduce casualties. At the same time, remote sensing applications enable researchers to study the planet and expand human understanding of environmental conditions.

Summary

Since prehistoric times, communication systems have evolved to serve new generations and the inherent needs of the population. While the sophistication of modern communication technology makes it possible to communicate more efficiently, expediently, economically, and effectively, negative repercussions emerge and must be addressed.

The information society made possible by communication technology brings with it both promises and perils. Citizens must use communication systems to evaluate the assets and liabilities of new technologies and create positive futures. New techniques for sending and receiving messages have the potential to transcend borders and interconnect cultures. Likewise, they have the capability of transforming human lives and conditions in ways that are both unappealing and undemocratic. It is the responsibility of people to understand this technological venture and play a determining role in its future. In the words of Edward Wenk:

> Tomorrow, we should expect more technology, not less. To shape that future we need to acquire this sharper image of technology as more than technique or products. It entails a tangled skein of familiar social processes, communication networks, and institutions, along with natural processes and technical facilities, a blend of science and human values. (Wenk, 1986, p. 12)

References

Compaine, B. M. (Ed.). (1988). *Issues in new information technology.* Norwood, NJ: Ablex Publishing.

Dizard, W. P. (1982). *The coming information age: An overview of technology, economics, and politics.* New York: Longman, Inc.

Forsdale, L. (1981). *Perspectives on communication* . Reading, MA: Addison-Wesley Publishing.

Frey, R. E. (1987, November). *Is there a philosophy of technology?* Paper presented at the 74th Mississippi Valley Industrial Teacher Education Conference, Chicago, IL.

Gandy, O. H., Jr., & Simmons, C. E. (1986). Technology, privacy and the democratic process. *Critical Studies in Mass Communication, 3*(2), 155-168.

Hendricks, R. W., & Sterry, L. F. (1987). *Communication technology: Know-how that extends our ability to communicate.* Menomonie, WI: T & E Publications.

Hirsch, E. D., Jr. (1988). *Cultural literacy: What every American needs to know.* New York: Vintage Books.

Mitcham, C. (1980). Philosophy of technology. In P. T. Durbin (Ed.). *A guide to the culture of science, technology, and medicine,* pp. 282-363. New York: Free Press.

Murphy, B. (1983). *The world wired up: Unscrambling the new communications puzzle.* London: Comedia Publishing Group.

National Science Board Commission of Precollege Education in Mathematics, Science and Technology. (1983). *Educating Americans for the 21st century.* Washington, DC: National Science Foundation.

Office of Technology Assessment. (1982). *Informational technology: its impact on American education* (Library of Congress Catalog No. 82-600608). Washington, DC: U. S. Government Printing Office.

Office of Technology Assessment. (1985). *Information technology and R & D: Critical trends and issues* (Library of Congress Catalog No. 84-601150). Washington, DC: U. S. Government Printing Office.

Salvaggio, J. L. (Ed.). (1989). *The information society: Economic, social, and structural issues.* Hillsdale, NJ: Lawrence Erlbaum Associates, Publishers.

Schwartz, T. (1981). *Media: The second god.* New York: Random House.

Serafini, S., & Andrieu, M. (1980). *The information revolution and its implications for Canada.* Hull, Quebec, Canada: Canadian Government Publishing Centre.

Shannon, C., & Weaver, W. (1949). *The mathematical theory of communication.* Urbana: University of Illinois Press.

Slack, J. D., & Fejes, F. (Eds.). (1987). *The ideology of the information age.* Norwood, NJ: Ablex Publishing.

Sommerlad, E. L. (1975). *National communication systems: Some policy options.* Paris, France: Unesco Press.

Tenner, E. (1988). Bad news for trees. *Computerworld, 22*(22), 53-57.

Thomas, L. (1979). *The medusa and the snail: More notes of a biology watcher.* New York: Viking Press.

United States Department of Commerce. (1988). *Statistical abstract of the United States* (108th ed.). Washington, DC: U. S. Government Printing Office.

Wakefield, R. (1986). Home computers and families. *The Futurist, 20*(5), 18-22.

Wenk, E., Jr. (1986). *Tradeoffs: Imperatives of choice in a high-tech world.* Baltimore, MD: John Hopkins University Press.

Williams, F. (Ed.). (1988). *Measuring the information society.* Newbury Park, CA: Sage Publications.

Chapter 2

COMMUNICATION SYSTEMS IN BUSINESS, INDUSTRY, AND GOVERNMENT

Frank Trocki
Professor
Center for Continuing Education
Northeastern University
Boston, MA

Corporate and Governmental Communication Systems

Communication is vital to the success of business, industry or government. Sociologists have advanced one definition of communication; it involves a behavioral situation in which someone transmits a message to someone else with a conscious intent to affect the latter's behavior. In plainer terms, this definition supplies the essential parts of any communication -- a source, a receiver, and a message -- and includes the prospect of control. As the source of a business communication, one has control over the information transmitted and the form in which it is transmitted. The form of the information affects the objective reception of the message and the subjective perception of both the message and the sender as the source.

Control of both reception and perception is a great asset for the corporate communicator, but neglecting this control can also be a great liability. For example, consider a situation in which two competing companies have submitted written bids for a large contract. Both proposals include a requested cost analysis of alternate contracts. The firms are equal in price, quality of product, service and ability to deliver. Imagine that the proposal of firm A has been typewritten, and it contains misspellings, strikeovers, inconsistent margins and line spacing. Lists of figures have not been broken out of the text and, although the requested cost analysis is provided, it is simply described in paragraph form within the main text of the proposal.

Firm B, on the other hand, has submitted a proposal generated on an electronic publishing system. There are no misspelled words, all margins and spacing are consistent, and the type is of near-typeset quality. Lists of figures are broken out and organized into columns. Furthermore, the requested cost analysis has been depicted in a simple and well-rendered graphic.

Which firm won the contract? By recognizing the opportunity to control both reception and perception, firm B submitted a proposal that not only provided information but also provided a physical representation (a design) that imparted the impression of a firm that was organized, detail oriented, and skilled in communication. Firm A, even though its proposal was equal in substance to that of firm B, neglected its opportunity to fully control the communication and, as a result, was perceived second rate.

To extend the argument further, remember the saying that a picture is worth a thousand words? It is also true that images are the only universal language. Imagine you are standing before a group of twenty people, each understanding a different language. There are no interpreters available. It would be difficult to communicate, with just words, the information that you have two factories in Mexico and three factories in Ireland. However, displaying an outline map of Mexico with two factory symbols and a map of Ireland with three factory symbols, would probably convey the message.

Each of the above examples demonstrates the important fact that effective communication relies on content, form, presentation and delivery. Individuals who are involved in creating, designing, producing and disseminating information must be aware of the importance of these elements and how they affect the "bottom line" of the company. Due to technological advances in both computer hardware and software and other communication devices this awareness must include virtually everyone who is involved in information processing.

As illustrated in Figure 2.1, corporate and governmental communications can be classified as either internal/external communication or for-profit or not-for-profit documentation. According to Alex Henderson (Malina, 1987) of Prudential-Bache Securities, the typical Fortune 500 company spends between twenty to forty million dollars per year on documentation, which represents six to ten percent of total company costs.

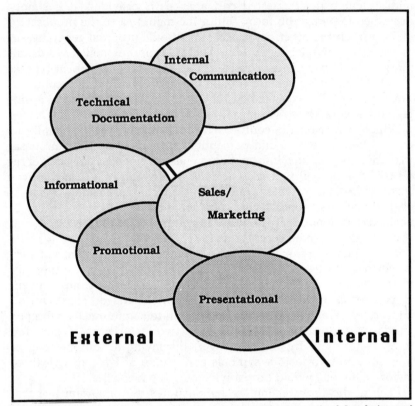

Figure 2.1: Types of corporate documentation created for internal and external use.

Further, companies in 1985 generated over 2.5 trillion pages of material. By 1990 they will be producing over 4 trillion pages of manuals, reports, internal documents, and other not-for-profit documents like product brochures, fact sheets, customer newsletters, bulletins and updates. These figures do not represent the additional trillion of pages of the commercial communication sector which includes newspaper, magazine and book industries.

Evolution of Corporate/Governmental Communication Systems

As with other inventions, the development and success of sophisticated communication systems depends on not a single invention but the fortuitous coming together of several key technologies.

As Gutenberg assembled the main components of the letterpress printing process: type production, a suitable ink, a press, and paper into a practical system for the generation and distribution of information; corporations such as Xerox, Digital, IBM, and Apple have combined the technology and techniques of networking, office automation, high resolution printer/copiers, scanners, text/graphics workstations and memory devices to give people working in corporations and government agencies the ability to electronically create, produce, share, distribute and store information. Created by Frank Romano (1988), Figure 2.2 illustrates this evolution and details the technological complexity of the system.

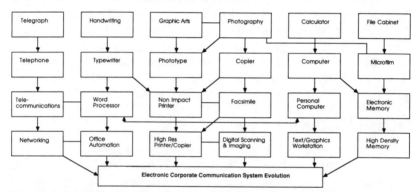

Figure 2.2: Technological relationships supporting corporate communication systems.

Several key inventions and innovations from this scheme have contributed to the present state of the art. However, several will continue to contribute and significantly impact communication systems of the future.

Corporate/Governmental Applications

Creation and development of communications in the noncommercial environment are driven by the habits of the existing organization. Although the relative shape of an organization varies from case to case, it can be generally assumed that work flow in an organization is subject to many more intangibles than work being processed in the production department of a commercial publisher. This is because corporations consist of a network of operations (or departments), many of which influence the content and design of documents that must be produced. In a typical corporation, it is possible for changes to be made to a document at virtually every stage in the review process, a condition that is difficult to avoid or manage. The best solution is to develop and implement a system that is highly tolerant of this process and that can be managed by people who understand the organization's work and priorities. Several types of noncommercial publishing categories are described.

Corporate Communication

Corporate communication includes the production of internal reports, requests for proposals, marketing and sales literature, customer service documentation, personnel manuals, internal newsletters and bulletins, and countless other documents that are present in the every day-to-day operation of an organization. This type of communication production is not-for-profit, in contrast to the production of newsletters, research reports, and other publications sold to customers. It is also distinguished from technical document production, which requires special work flow and production management.

Technical Documentation

The development of technical documentation generally follows a rigid pattern of development and control than most other types of corporate communication. Typically, the technical documentation department is a centralized group that is run like a production shop. Work is closely supervised and tracked, a priority system is in place, and a quality control system is enforced.

The expenses of providing documentation to support a company's products are often unappreciated for their share of product cost. Boston University's Center for Effective Communication estimated that between five to ten percent of a technical product's cost lies in the documentation behind it. Boeing Corporation, according to *Industry Week* magazine (March, 1987), spends over $2 billion for technical documentation each year -- a figure large enough to be placed well up on the Fortune 500 list all by itself! Similarly, just under 8% of the cost of a General Dynamics ballistic missile submarine is in its supporting documentation. This includes documentation to research it, design it, introduce it to the marketplace, train employees, organize technical support and very importantly support the end user. It is clear that such an expense of doing business demands constant attention and consideration of the application of evolving technologies.

The importance of rigid controls for the creation of technical material should not be overlooked. An example of the importance of quality control and accurate information is in the story behind the crash of a Turkish Airways DC-10 near Paris. An airline mechanic, using an outdated manual, had incorrectly maintained a cargo door which failed and caused the deaths of 310 passengers. Similar demands for complete and accurate product technical documentation are found in the chemical, medical, pharmaceutical and other industries. Industries which will spend virtually any amount of money to insure accuracy of their documentation.

Financial Communication

Most financial communications are created entirely in-house and do not require outside services. Many of the documents are created in response to business needs that emerge daily: client inquiries, investment proposals, analysis of investments opportunities. In addition, there are numerous periodic reports required to keep clients informed. The most important requirements as illustrated in Figure 2.3 are: fast turnaround, the highest quality possible given the time allowed, integrated text and graphics, data-base driven graphics, statistics, and tables.

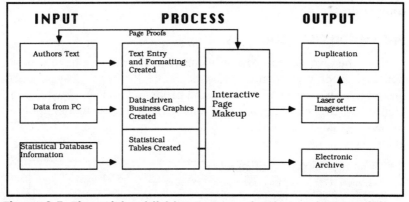

Figure 2.3: Financial publishing communication system model.

Not identified, but becoming significantly more important to the financial industry is information security. Due to computer use, recent white collar crimes of securities information trading on Wall Street to typographers/typesetters selling futures information is causing managers of data to redesign the flow of information to editorial, design and production personnel.

Insurance Communication

The insurance industry is a highly regulated business, having to abide by rules and regulations imposed by state insurance regulatory bodies and by the government. These rules and regulations set forth specifications and standards for published documents. In addition, all insurance companies, large or small, have a broad spectrum of publishing applications that are determined by individual department needs, agents, agencies, and policyholders. Deadlines and specified time frames are also built into insurance company applications.

One insurance company, John Hancock, has totally restructured and redesigned their corporate communication direction. Several million dollars have been spent in an attempt to offer departments throughout the company electronic design and publishing capabilities. Additionally, an electronic communication design group has been created to serve the needs of all users wanting to develop sophisticated documentation in a variety of output formats. They produce traditional print media as well as color thermal prints, color copying, color overheads and 35mm slides for presentation graphics. Over 245 departments within John Hancock utilize this group for the design and production of both internal and external corporate communication.

Production Characteristics

All of the examples of communication just described have production and graphic elements that will dictate the type of systems required that will effectively create and produce them. As illustrated in Figure 2.4, the following assumptions about these elements apply to the average corporate/governmental environment and are offered as a guide.

CHARACTERISTIC	REQUIREMENT
Document Length	Short to medium: 1 to 100 pages
Volume	Low to medium: 1to 100 copies per page
Document Life Cycle	Short: most documents used only once
Quality of Document Appearance	Business quality: photocopy or 300 dpi laser image
Graphic Elements	Growing in importance and complexity
Number of Formats	Many: though not complex
Format Layout	Mostly uniform layout: developed standards
Color	Usually black & white but color is becoming popular
Forms Creation	Approximately 35% are forms
Interfacing	High: 50% or more documents require input from other systems

Figure 2.4: Characteristics of corporate/government documents.

26

Document Length: most corporate communication is short or moderate in length. Letters, memos, and operational reports are generally short, whereas business plans, internal reports, policy manuals, and other documentation can often range between 20 and 100 pages. Few office documents exceed 100 pages. Of course, it is common knowledge that many government reports may be several thousand pages long and involve these being presented in bound volumes.

Volume: the number of copies made of office communication fall into the low and medium ranges. Individual letters, memos, and reports often go to only one recipient; many other documents are circulated to a closed group of individuals that generally does not exceed 100. Exceptions to this rule include organization-wide bulletins and announcements, but these generally account for a very small percentage of all the documents produced in an organization.

Document life-cycle: the vast majority of office documents have a very short life cycle. Many examples such as memos, activity reports, and announcements are used only once and never revised. A second class of documents has a medium life cycle and includes such examples as business plans, client reports, marketing releases and other materials that undergo many changes during a developmental period that can range from weeks to months.

Quality of appearance: the degree of quality required in the average corporate office environment can almost always be satisfied by a 300 dot per inch image, the use of a limited number of type styles, and minimum requirements for line and word spacing.

Graphic element complexity: today, graphic elements for the majority of business communication are not highly complex and include such things as business charts and graphs. Many of these are currently created using personal computers. With the availability of illustration and graphics features on publishing systems, the quality and complexity of graphics, even in common office documents, has increased dramatically. Until now, only a few departments such as marketing were interested in using advanced art and layout features. Marketing may still be the only group in need of truly professional illustrations and photographic work in their communication, but most departments can find many ways to utilize the high-quality line art, charts, and graphs that can be created with the typical text and graphics composition. Suggested applications include the creation of organizational charts, workflow diagrams, systems diagrams, floor plans, forms, and general line art used to illustrate internal reports.

Number of formats: corporate and governmental communications are characterized by a wide variety of document types, hence a high number of formats required. These may not be terribly complex formats, but the ability to manage document production with such a wide range of options available can be challenging.

Format layout: most communication produced in the office employ uniform layouts (sometimes referred to as templates) that can be applied to other documents of the same type. For example, operations reports, accounting reports, business plans, and related documents usually look the same each time they are produced. The increasing use of text and graphics composition systems, however, will inspire the use of more sophisticated layouts and graphics in even the most familiar office documents, thus requiring a more page intensive approach to layout for many applications that previously did not require such complexity. The area where a more page intensive layout is already important is marketing where promotional literature, customer newsletters, and other documents employing a more complex set of graphic elements are produced.

Color requirements: the majority of publications produced in corporate or governmental offices are predominately black and white, requiring no color whatsoever. Traditionally, two-color and four-color communication originated and were produced from the marketing or sales department. However, with color extensions to popular software page-layout programs and low cost color scanners, other departmental units are beginning to produce colorful documents.

Forms requirements: although an organization may reproduce many copies of forms, the actual number of original forms that must be designed and maintained is typically low; less than 35%. However, in certain departments (personnel), governmental agencies or industries (such as the insurance industry) the design and production of forms may actually predominate the communication publishing process.

Interfacing requirements: a communication system in any organization will probably need to interface with other systems in an organization that provides input for documents. These sources of input range from word processors, personal computers, and electronic typewriters to minicomputers and mainframes. The complexity of this issue in the typical corporate office results in a high interfacing need in which as many as 50% or more of the documentations will derive all or part of their contents from other system sources. The need to interface with other systems can be divided into three general groups by the nature of the information being input: text information, statistical database information and graphics information.

The majority of interfacing involves the transfer of text information from word-processing systems, personal computers, optical character recognition devices (OCR) and modem transfer. Software available for the PC allows desktop scanners to be used as OCR devices and are virtually error free.

Many companies access their main computer databases for information that will be placed into documents. This information covers a wide range of needs, from sales records to personnel files to parts catalogs and pricing tables, that are best maintained on a database. The need to interface with such statistical databases for communication purposes is of vital importance to large organizations, including state and federal offices.

Corporate/Governmental Communication Systems Characteristics

The previous sections identified the types of communication documents in the noncommercial environment and the production characteristics of these documents. It follows then, that these characteristics imply certain system requirements are needed to effectively produce documents. Based on these assumptions, communication systems for the development of corporate communication should include the following characteristics and capabilities.

Microcomputer-based Publishing Capabilities

Software. Four categories of software, or a single system which integrates all four applications, are needed: word processing, graphics, page-composition and layout, and networking. The nature of the graphics program depends on the company's requirements. Data-driven graphics produce charts from a database or spreadsheet of statistics. An art or drawing package allows the creation of line art, flowcharts, and other drawings.

The system should provide for text editing and composition features, as well as graphics creation and composition features. Batch pagination to handle highly uniform document formats such as letters, memos, and reports should be included. The ability to size and manipulate the appearance of graphics is also important.

Interactive text and graphics layout are available using icon-based, menu-driven software and full-page display with a mouse/stylus controller. This type of system is ideal for page-intensive layout typical in the corporate, financial, and insurance environments. It permits the greatest control over page-intensive design work while at the same time allowing flexibility in the design of communication elements.

Selective repagination is important so that a section in the middle of a document can be repaginated without affecting the entire document. Page numbers in technical documents are often complex and include codes that help identify the purpose and placement of a page within a manual. The system must be capable of handling long, compound, alphanumeric page numbers and to generate indexes and tables of contents based upon them.

Hardware. System capabilities are introduced in corporations in a couple of different ways. The technology can be distributed -- each department is provided with what it needs on an individual basis -- or every department can be linked to a common system that serves the needs of the entire organization. The size and complexity of the overall operation usually determines which approach is utilized.

The individual or standalone approach usually implies the use of a personal computer, some page-layout software, and an output device. A laser printer is adequate for most corporate communication needs. Resolution of 300 by 300 dots per inch (dpi) is satisfactory for reproduction of text and graphic elements. Speeds of 8 to 20 copies per minute (cpm) are adequate. An intermediate speed, 20 to 50 cpm, is recommended for technical documentation. High speed, 50 to 150 cpm, is recommended if catalogs and lists are published directly from a database maintained on a mainframe computer system.

Networking. Linked, networked or multi-user configurations are much more common in corporate and governmental environments and have numerous advantages over individual departmental configurations. For example, users can share common resources such as printers, mass storage, and software as well as the ability to communicate through electronic mail. Additionally, an electronic production cycle can be developed whereby work flow from various sources can be channeled to one common production point for pagination and output. This is especially important if the organization wants to insure quality and format standards.

Local area networks have been divided into four distinct categories based on application: broadband networks for high-speed data transfer between mainframe processors; broadband networks for factory automation; general-purpose baseband/broadband networks for office applications; and entry-level networks (largely baseband) designed especially to link personal computers.

Microcomputer LAN Categories

Although the actual operations of microcomputer LANs are diverse, a look at their media and topologies can identify a functional, if arbitrary, means of categorizing and analyzing them. Microcomputer local area networks can be considered as fitting into one of the following classes.

Large-Scale Microcomputer LANs are capable of supporting up to 20 or more users in a busy environment without severe response time degradation. The systems are usually baseband types, using bus or star topologies for their design. Multiple file, disc, and peripheral servers can be supported, and these are often microcomputers configured with hard discs and extra memory for handling the LAN software. For disc-intensive applications, proprietary, dedicated server-devices are recommended for use as the primary network hosting device.

Intermediate-Scale Microcomputer LANs are suitable for environments of up to 10 microcomputers under the same heavily loaded conditions. These networks are also based upon a central server for data and peripheral access, which again may be the vendor's dedicated server, or an appropriately configured microcomputer, as above.

Entry-Level Microcomputer LANs are generally low-cost options aimed at the small business that needs to link no more than five microcomputers together economically. Limited Microcomputer LANs are defined as miscellaneous networking schemes designed for linking workstations and peripherals together. They are limited in the number of devices that they can support, usually less than ten, and their low cost makes them ideal for such tasks. For example, a small office that wants to share an expensive printer or plotter between two micros and do a limited amount of file sharing and messaging can now do so.

Corporate Communication via LANs

For organizations with internal graphic communications departments, a LAN can serve as the link between the graphics department and different departments in the company. The individual group, (e.g., marketing, advertising, sales, public relations) creates its own text files and shares its own printers for printing draft copies, correspondence, and straightforward text documents for low-volume distribution. Text files written for documents that have complex page layouts, are intended for high-volume distribution, or are to be merged with illustrations, halftones, or charts can be transmitted over the network to the graphics department, where the text file is merged with the other elements using an electronic publishing system.

A LAN offers increased communication capabilities. Electronic mail on a LAN establishes an effective communication link between employees. Likewise, multiple copies of files to be distributed to different users on the network can be sent directly from the workstation, without using the copier and distributing the copies by hand.

A LAN may also include gateways to other computer networks. Presently, micro-to-mainframe links are also of particular interest to many corporations where users desire access to data on the mainframe. Here a microcomputer LAN can streamline users' access to mainframe resources by eliminating redundant connection hardware and, in some instances, easing the mainframe's burden of communications overhead.

Perhaps more importantly, a LAN makes it possible to create a central, shared depository for common files. An electronic database of frequently used forms, blank charts, mailing lists, and document formats that can be accessed by anyone on the network provides an efficient means of retrieval for the creation of periodically produced, single-format documents. In many cases, it also allows a company to establish for the first time standard forms for files and documents, and to guarantee a minimum of deviation from those standards.

In the completely electronic office, the LAN can provide nearly instantaneous desk-to-desk communication, allowing the terminal to function as typewriter, copier, and "telephone" for internal use. Ultimately, the office local area network can eliminate the need to circulate paper documents, by distributing schedules and memoranda almost instantly to each worker's terminal.

Electronic Media Delivery

Electronic delivery of information continues to gain acceptance as an alternative to the printed page. Due to the fact that more and more options for electronic delivery have increased in recent years more and more computer users are accessing databases and conducting searches. While electronic delivery is not yet a mainstream activity, its use is increasing in all organizations.

The costs associated with the electronic generation of information are decreasing. As an example, with optical discs, a million pages of computer-readable information can be "printed" for under $20, every

60 seconds, at the highest standards of data accuracy. Additionally, telecommunications costs have decreased, the increased prevalence of packet-switching networks (Telenet, Tymet), and the introduction of local area networks (LAN's) are forces that are helping to challenge the printed word.

Videotex services, on-line databases, optical discs are just some of the electronic delivery media now available to individuals. Although some of these methods have been used for a decade or more, such methods have just become commercially available or economically viable.

For nearly three decades, information has been sent electronically from centrally located mainframe computers to remote terminals. It was during 1957 that Scantlin Electronics (now Quotron Systems, Inc.) first sent stock quotes electronically to brokerage houses, banks, insurance companies, and other financial institutions. Since then, the electronic delivery of information has undergone phenomenal techno-logical change and financial growth. For example, *InfoWorld* (1988) reports there are now over 3,000 different on-line databases in use today (collections of facts in machine-readable form). These cover everything from Wall Street to wine and from the opera to baseball. Those are just the public databases. There are as many, if not more proprietary databases that companies use for internal information exchange.

Increased Access to Databases

As Rubin (1986) pointed out, General Electric in 1964 commer-cialized the concept of time-sharing which refers to the simultaneous use of a centralized computer from remote sites. The technology enabled companies that couldn't afford, or justify, the cost of buying their own mainframe computers to perform data processing. Compa-nies, including GE, Burroughs, and McDonnell Douglas, that were already using large multi-million dollar mainframe computers for their own needs, subsequently made excess system capacity and processing time available to thousands of smaller companies.

As this "remote computing" industry grew, so did telecommunica-tion networks, which permitted electronic communication to occur more economically than via telephone lines. Other aspects of on-line delivery systems were also developed -- including software, protocols, and standards that allowed database developers to avoid "reinventing the wheel" for each system. In effect, the remote computing industry in large part paved the way for the birth of the database industry, which uses these same delivery mechanisms.

Also crucial to the birth of the on-line database industry was the emergence of computerized typesetting. In the early 1960's publishers such as The National Library of Medicine turned to computers to create indexing and abstracting publications. Subsequently, on-line information vendors, which used computerized phototypesetting tapes to create bibliographic databases, were born. Companies such as Bibliographic Retrieval Services (BRS), DIALOG Information Technologies, and System Development Corporation (SDC) formatted the magnetic tapes so the information could be searched interactively and then transferred the information to discs (Romano, 1986).

These early on-line services primarily served researchers and librarians, who used their databases to locate publications. Later, in the mid-seventies, consumer and business-oriented services emerged, including CompuServe, Dow Jones News/Retrieval, and The Source. Still, the industry grew slowly and remained the province of information professionals.

The database industry looks much different than it did just a decade ago. The proliferation of microcomputers and the availability of less expensive telecommunication systems led to a growing appreciation for information's power and importance. According to Market Intelligence Research Company of Palo Alto, California (1988) the industry grew 40 to 50 percent per year between 1982 and 1985. Growth has since slowed, but still attained a respectable 19.6 percent in 1986 and 23 percent in 1987. Market Intelligence predicts that, impelled by the proliferation of microcomputers, the on-line database market will reach $4.13 billion by 1990.

Much of this growth comes from the corporate community, for which the high cost of database access is not an issue. Databases range from $6 per hour (e.g., Tickerscreen, a discount brokerage service on CompuServe) when accessed during non-prime time hours, to the $300 per hour CLAIMS/U (patents) database from SDC. The average cost of on-line systems services average about $100 per hour. It is not surprising therefore, that corporate users account for 95% of the on-line industry's revenues.

A few years ago most databases provided only article abstracts or citations rather than the full text. This was always a major drawback, until recently. Due to the falling cost of computer memory and storage full-text databases are less expensive to utilize. Coupled with other optical media technology like videodiscs, CD-ROMs, and videotex complete book and magazine texts are becoming available to on-line databases at lower costs.

Audio Media

Laser-based audio compact discs (CD-A) bring to the home, automobile, train or bus dulcet tones heretofore heard only in concert halls. As a result, laser technology has turned the record industry from stagnation into vitality. Since their introduction in 1982, over 100 million audio discs have been sold world-wide, prompting some industry analysts to call the CD-A the most successful consumer product ever.

Audio discs succeed for three reasons: they offer better sound; there is but one standard for them; and they are affordable to the consumer market. Now, in the opinion of some experts, the technology may do more for people involved in the creation, production and dissemination of information than Gutenburg's printing press.

Optical Media

Optical media options include optical discs, based on audio-disc technology, videodiscs, and optical memory cards. The videodisc was the first optical technology that was widely available. Demonstrated in 1972 by Phillips in the Netherlands and MCA in Hollywood, the standard-sized disc holds up to thirty minutes of high quality video or up to 54,000 still frames on each side. A videodisc is prepared from a master videotape. Through a "mastering" process, the images and sounds are transferred to a disc. Mastering imprints the disc with microscopic pits, which a laser beam reads when the disc is played. Similar production methods are used to manufacture CD-ROMs.

Although videodiscs are perfectly suited to still and motion video storage, they are not as well suited to data storage. Consequently, videodiscs will be confined to those databases with a substantial graphic or photographic content. CD-ROM technology will largely supplant videodisc technology.

Videotex

Videotex is a generic term which describes an interactive, user-friendly computer system for information delivery, transaction processing, and user-to-user communication. Corporations have discovered that videotex can be a valuable tool for internal communications. By its very nature, corporate videotex is a closed system in which the organization defines not only the system, terminals and protocols to be used, but the user population as well. The purpose of a corporate videotex system highlights the basic functions of any videotex system: the management and delivery of information and services through an easy-to-use interface. Because videotex provides access to a variety of separate services and databases through a common interface it can be a useful tool for information-system end users.

Just imagine if there existed a corporate information system that managers could use with little or no training. Wouldn't it be convenient if this one system could give a company's employees access to electronic forms handling and the electronic mail system, as well as access to numeric databases and on-line text files? The vendors of videotex systems are developing and marketing corporate, or organizational, videotex systems based on the anticipated advantages of accessing a variety of services and information sources through a single system.

If such claims are legitimate, videotex may prove to be an important technological component in two of the hottest areas of information systems. It has the potential to help integrate existing on-line systems by making it a useful office automation tool and it has ability to give casual users access to numeric databases.

To access a videotex system, a user typically connects a terminal device to the videotex computer through a telephone line and interacts with the system by making keyword and menu selections. The main menu typically offers the user the choice of a variety of communication, transaction processing, and information retrieval options.

In addition, changes can also be expected in the user interface. Today, menu and keyboard choices are used to minimize the need for training and user manuals. Soon, developments in several areas of artificial intelligence will provide alternatives that will make menus seem rather archaic. Natural-language interfaces, knowledge system front ends, and voice input will combine to dramatically alter the meaning of the term user-friendly.

References

Brand, S. (1987). *The media lab: Inventing the future at MIT*. NY: Viking.

Doebler, P. (1988, August/September). Rely on the experts: A look at artificial intelligence in electronic publishing and printing. *EP&P, 3*(6), pp. 39-45.

Electronic publishing helps move the product. (1987, March). *Industry Week, 3*(11), pp. 67-68.

Field, A. R., Harris, C. L. (1986, August). The information business. *Business Week, 26*(32).

Finn, T. A., Stewart C. M. (1985). From consumer to organizational videotex: Will videotex find a home at the office. *Communication Yearbook 9*, Sage Publications.

Gecesi, J. (1983). *The architecture of videotex systems*. Englewood Cliffs, NJ: Prentice-Hall.

Gross, L. S. (1988). *Telecommunications: An Introduction to Electronic Media*. Dubuque, IA: Wm. C. Brown Publishers.

Kurz, P. (1989, January). From video to print. *Magazine: Design and Production, 5*(1), pp. 24-28.

Langenes, B., Bajarin, T. P. (1987). *Desktop publishing: Market, industry, and technology and outlook to 1990*. Santa Clara, CA: Creative Strategies Research International.

Malina, D. (1987, August/September). Electronic publishing: Mass firms plot to conquer the market. *Mass High Tech. 5*(24), pp. 1, 29-32.

McLean, B. (1987, August/September). What desktop publishing is not -- Defining system limitations. *EP&P, 2*(4), pp. 16-17.

Mooers, C. (1960, March). Mooers' law: Or why some retrieval systems are used and others are not. *American Documentation, 11*(3), pp. 11-15.

Romano, F. J. (1986). *Machine writing and typesetting*. Salem, NH: GAMA.

Romano, F. J. (1988, Spring). Putting together the puzzles in computer-aided publishing. *The S. Klein Computer Graphics Review*, pp. 67-77.

Trocki, F. R., Carter, W. T. (1988/89, Winter). Electronic publishing: A new dimension in document production. *Journal of Industrial Technology, 5*(1).

Uhlig, R., Faber, D. J., & Bair, J. (1979). *The office of the future*. Monograph Series of the International Council for Computer Communications. NY: Elsevier North-Holland Publishing Company.

Virkus, R. (1989, October). Planning the total publishing system. *Magazine: Design and Production, 5*(10).

Chapter 3

HISTORY OF COMMUNICATION CONTENT IN TECHNOLOGY EDUCATION

Janet L. Robb
Assistant Professor
and
Ronald E. Jones
Professor
Department of Industrial Technology
University of North Texas
Denton, Texas

Communication has been included, promoted, supported, and rationalized as part of technology education during numerous professional presentations, papers, workshops, meetings, and curriculum efforts. Often, the inclusion is based on such things as the popularity of the term or an assumption that it "simply needs to be included" because it is part of the study of technology. However, sound curriculum design must follow the selection of a major area of study which, in turn, should be based on some logical, rational basis of selection. For this rationale we are working under the assumption that:

1. Communication is the transfer of information, via technical means, and
2. Communication Technology is the study of the transfer of information via technical means.

These assumptions may also be construed as definitions. As definitions, they are broad and general, yet they provide focus. The key word on which to focus is the term "technical." Communication, in this technical sense, has been suggested in the literature as a necessary component in the study of technology.

DeVore, Maughan, and Griscom (1979) completed a major review of literature in an attempt to determine what, if any, was the influence

of technology on industrial arts subject matter. They stated that:
> A review of literature concerned with the study of technolo-
> gy indicated that the predominant organizational theme
> used by authors such as Kranzberg, Pursell, McHale, Fuller,
> Derry and Williams, Toffler, Ferkiss, Goldschmidt, Forbes,
> Brady, and Helman, among others, was systems . . . Occu-
> pations, skills, products change, and many times are elimi-
> nated entirely . . . whereas systems production . . .
> communication and transportation continue. (p. 189)

Lauda and McCrory (1986) helped emphasize the importance of communication in the curriculum when they stated, "Sociologists and anthropologists are quick to point out the need for communication. . . production . . . and transportation" (p. 21). They further cite that ". . . technology education curriculum. . . [must] be studied in the contexts of production, transportation and communication" (p. 34).

While the terms production, transportation, and communication seem clear enough, one problem that plagues our profession is that many traditional course names or areas of study often cause confusion. For example, there are existing categories of courses with names such as: materials (woods, metals), processes (welding, photography), physical phenomena (electricity, power), or generic phrases (graphic arts, woodworking, power technology).

Several organizers have been suggested for the study of technology. Among these are communication, production, manufacturing, construction, transportation, energy, and power. The organizers agreed upon by the Jackson's Mill group (Hales & Snyder, 1981) were communication, construction, manufacturing, and transportation. Their selection was based on the identification of the universal technical systems used by humans to adapt to their environment. Ray (1980) had earlier suggested that the principle of "human endeavor" be used to categorize our subject matter and also had identified the same four areas. Logically, these four areas are the "systems" that make up the study of technology. This same selection was included in the "Professional Improvement Plan" (Starkweather, 1983) and the *Standards for Technology Education Programs* (Dugger, 1985).

Communication, construction, manufacturing, and transportation systems are readily accepted by students as relevant in today's society to help prepare them for tomorrow. Sound, rational curriculum design for technology education has resulted from a focus on these systems. One may speculate that these will be primary systems for human survival in the future since it has been through these four systems that humans adapted to their environment in the past. This, then, is a logical basis for selecting these particular systems as content areas of study.

With the exception of some minor variations of the name, communication technology has been consistently included in the curriculum efforts of states that have changed to technology-based programs. Examples of these variations have included visual communication, graphic communication, communication systems, industrial communication, and electronic communication, to name a few. Regardless of the name selected, the content, for the most part, reflects the content identified in the early research on communication technology. Other terms seem to add limitations and restrictions on the content to be addressed. One may assume that the selection of names may be based more on terms that have a familiar ring to them or for political reasons, rather than based on actual research into the area. Regardless of the number of terms, communication technology appears to be prevalent as the most popular term used to reflect the total technological system of communication. The term communication technology accurately and best reflects the research, background, and curricular intent of technology education.

Historical Connections of Technology and Communication

Throughout the literature on the history and development of civilization, technology is repeatedly cited as the key element to transformation and advancement. Bell (1973) identified five unique ways in which technology has brought about social transformations. One statement was "the revolutions in transportation and communication, as a consequence of technology, have created new economic interdependencies and new social interactions." The significance and indispensable nature of communication technology was further emphasized by Burke (1978) when he wrote, "the last time a world empire fell apart it was Roman, and there, too, the last fragments of the Roman province of Gaul, which had broken up into several small kingdoms, were held together by a communication network which preserved some of the imperial administration techniques" (p. 82). DeVore refers to communication as "the third major technological system required for successful industrialization. . ." (1980, p. 192).

As Kranzberg and Pursell (1967) pointed out in the preface to *Technology in Western Civilization Volume 1*, although the history of technology is considered a branch of social history, "at the same time, technology has had its own internal history . . . " (p. ii). This internal history deals primarily with actual technological devices and processes; what Kranzberg and Pursell refer to as "hardware." The technological devices and processes, or hardware, of communication have played an integral role in the growth and development of society at every stage of its evolution.

> The ability of man to communicate with ease helps to distinguish him from all other creatures that inhabit this planet. The pattern of development of methods of communication can well form an index of his individual and social progress. The extent to which he has been able to communicate, store, and retrieve information is the bold and measurable mark of his progress in recent centuries. (Dibner, 1967, p. 452)

The communication means available in 1492 were such that it took six months to notify Queen Isabella I of Spain that Columbus had discovered the New World. In 1865 it took 12 weeks for the British government to receive news that President Abraham Lincoln had been shot. In 1969 it took less than 2 seconds for the world to receive news that Neil Armstrong safely landed on the moon. In fact, the world was able to witness that event, and hear the first words spoken on the moon, from a distance of approximately 320,000 kilometers. All this has been possible as a result of communication technologies (Jones & Robb, 1986).

Curricular Perspectives in Industrial Arts

Communication, as a part of the study of technology, is apparent throughout our professional literature and has been alluded to in other literature as well. A major reference to communication as part of technology and related to curriculum, was in Warner's feature presentation and paper to the American Industrial Arts Association Convention, entitled, "A Curriculum to Reflect Technology" (1947). Warner stated that "We examined the census and other economic data to discover five or more large divisions of subject matter resources, namely: *Power, Transportation, Manufacture, Construction, and Communication . . .* " (p. 3). Latimer (1979), in writing about Warner, stated that "The curriculum was derived from a socioeconomic analysis of technology rather than by trade and job analysis.

The subject matter classifications included power, transportation, manufacturing, construction, communication, and management" (p. 27).

Major Curriculum Efforts

The curriculum efforts of the 1960's provided the first concentrated inclusion of communication into major curriculum efforts. Cochran (1970) completed a major study of curricula in an attempt to compare selected contemporary programs of the era. In his review of Interpretation of Industry Programs, Occupational Family Programs, and Technology Oriented Programs, seven curriculum efforts were identified as containing specific references for including communication. The contribution of these curriculum efforts to the study of communication follows.

American Industry Project. The project was developed by Wesley Face and Eugene Flug and funded by the Ford Foundation. The objectives of this project focused on the ability ". . . (1) to develop an understanding of those concepts that apply directly to industry, and (2) to develop the ability to solve problems related to industry" (p. 40). What resulted was that "An analysis of industry revealed thirteen common concept areas that were prevalent throughout industry. These included communication" (p. 40).

Georgia Plan for Industrial Arts. Donald Hackett, working with graduate classes at Georgia Southern College in 1960, prepared a manuscript adopted into a program by the Georgia Department of Education, which included curriculum efforts "to help prepare individuals to meet the requirements of our technological culture" (p. 46). This program model was multi-layered with a variety of options. At the seventh grade level, one option existed where "boys and girls, take the newly developed courses in communications, manufacturing, and transportation to become familiar with the role of man in using technology in the basic industries" (pp. 46-49).

Orchestrated Systems Approach. Lewis Yoho developed the framework ". . . to develop in the individual those societal competencies essential to understand and participate in the production and consumption of goods and services" (p. 53). Toward this goal, the program focused on ". . . manufacturing, construction, service, salvage, and industrial-technical communication" (p. 53).

Galaxy Plan for Career Preparation. In an attempt to form an exploratory analysis of occupations, Arthur Elges summarized the activities of a Detroit group of educators. "The basic premise of the

Galaxy Plan is that occupational groups can be classified into four major clusters. They include the following: (1) Materials and processes, (2) Visual communications, (3) Energy and propulsion, and (4) Personal services" (p. 61).

Occupational, Vocational and Technical Program (OVT). The OVT program was developed in the Pittsburgh schools to ". . . provide experiences related to the world of work from the sixth grade through grade fourteen . . . The broad areas . . . at sixth grade level relate to the concepts of human relations, products, communications, and economics" (p. 64). At the seventh, eighth, ninth, and tenth grade levels the subject groupings consistently included visual communications.

Alberta Plan. Henry Ziel, developed the Alberta Plan ". . . based on the premise of making industrial arts a synthesizing educational process in a multiple-activity environment" (p. 75). This plan was divided into four phases. Phase I provided students experiences in a variety of areas of which graphic arts was included. Phase II introduced the study of major technologies which included graphic communication, and Phase III allowed for simulation of industrial situations that ". . . focus upon organizational structures, decision making, communications, and authority configurations" (p. 77).

Industrial Arts: A Study of Industry and Technology (The Maryland Plan). ". . . Donald Maley developed a method of organizing special classes in industrial education based upon research and experimentation" (p. 80). The program was designed to start at the seventh grade level and to continue through the ninth grade. At the seventh grade the program ". . . focuses on units dealing with tools and machines, power and energy, and communication and transportation" (p. 81).

Other Influential Devlopments

The 28th Yearbook of the American Council on Industrial Arts Teacher Education, entitled *Industrial Arts Education: Retrospect, Prospect* (Martin, 1979) also contained a series of reviews of curriculum efforts from the 1960's and 70's. These reviews included programs similar to those reviewed by Cochran, with few exceptions. One exception of note is the Enterprise: Man and Technology program. In an attempt to focus on the total American enterprise system, the program was ". . . proposed as an alternative to industrial arts . . .

Initial experiences were designed to provide broad, exploratory occupational experiences in visual communications . . ." (Householder, 1979, p. 119).

Also included in the 28th Yearbook was a more in-depth look at The Maryland Plan. This review went beyond the curriculum efforts of The Maryland Plan at the junior high level and explained its premise for senior high school programs, as well. Maley, in writing about the development of the Maryland Plan, cited, "The principal thrust of the senior high school program centered around a number of problem areas facing mankind. These included . . . communications . . ." (1979, p. 139).

Practices in the Schools

Despite the significant role of communication in the development of civilization and our advancement to a technological society and the continued inclusion of communication in the major curriculum efforts of the 60's and 70's, little evidence exists to show that communication as a subject area was, in actuality, included in typical curriculums. It wasn't until the mid- to late-70's that significant events took place contributing to the inclusion of communication technology in the public school curriculum.

Developments in Technology Education

A gradual trend away from a focus on industry and toward the study of technology and technological systems began in the mid-1970's. The vast majority of curriculum research, thinking, and development in technology education has materialized and been recognized since that time. Two events, the development of the first undergraduate technology teacher education program and the first national conference specifically focusing on technology education, served to provide impetus for progress.

Work began in 1975 at Eastern Illinois University (EIU) to develop a contemporary technology-based program for teacher education. A major curriculum effort was launched and "new" classes were offered beginning in 1976, with the first graduates of the technology education program receiving degrees in 1979 (Lauda & Wright, 1983). The course offerings in the new technology education degree program ". . . represent curriculum based on the adaptive systems of production, communication, and energy/power" (p. 19).

The first national conference specifically addressing technology education was held at Eastern Illinois University in 1980 and was called Symposium '80. The proceedings of that symposium provided the framework and a basis for continuing dialogue on all aspects of technology education. The concept of the symposium was successful and subsequent symposia have been held annually. Proceedings from each symposium have continued to support the research base for technology education (Wright, Ed., 1980). One-third of Symposium '80 agenda focused on communication technology. Speakers were asked to address questions relating to communication technology and its relationship with technology education. Formal papers discussing communication were presented by Frank Trocki, Earl Yarborough, and Barry DuVall. In addition, communication, as an integral part of technology education, was identified in presentations by Donald P. Lauda, Robert A. Daiber, M. James Bensen, and Paul W. DeVore (Wright, Ed., 1980).

Landmark Efforts

Other events continued to verify the study of technology and the inclusion of communication technology as an integral part of the technology education curriculum. The following events are worth mentioning.

Jackson's Mill Industrial Arts Curriculum Theory. This was one of the earlier and most widely-accepted efforts to identify technological systems (Hales & Snyder, 1981). This document "A Curriculum Theory for Industrial Arts," became known as the Jackson's Mill Curriculum Theory due to the meeting location in West Virginia. That meeting, and the subsequent document, provided a cohesiveness and direction with the identification of the four systems of manufacturing, construction, transportation, and communication as curriculum organizers.

The Illinois Plan. This project, which began around 1981, emphasized the study of technology via technology education in an articulated program K-adult (Illinois Plan, 1983; Erekson & Scarborough, 1983). The curriculum model was based on the study of technology utilizing the technological systems model (Jones, 1983). The primary emphasis was on the development of units devoted to the study of the technological systems at the ninth and tenth grade in high school (Koester, 1983). One of the system courses developed was communication and it focused on the resources, processes, applications, and impacts of the technologies within the realm of communication.

New York Futuring Project. A massive curriculum effort was launched in New York that became known as "The Futuring Project" (Hacker & Lister, 1985). This effort focused on changing and influencing legislation to mandate the study of technology for middle school students in New York. Communication was recognized as an important component of the statewide curriculum adopted.

Standards for Technology Education. With a grant and direction of the U. S. Department of Education Virginia Polytechnic Institute and State University developed *Standards for Industrial Arts* (Dugger, 1980). This project was subsequently revised to focus on technology education. The document provided a basis to evaluate programs and, for the first time, identified standards for programs in technology education (Dugger et al., 1985). The content area of communication as a part of technology education curriculum was included among the standards for evaluating programs.

Industry and Technology Education. This was the title of a document produced by a group that studied the Jackson's Mill curriculum theory and attempted to formulate a curriculum model reflective of the Jackson's Mill efforts. The outgrowth of that meeting resulted in the development of three different curriculum models based on size of school. This group chose to focus on the term industrial technology, but continued to utilize the organizers common to technology education as the basis for their models (Technical Foundation of America, 1984).

Implementing Technology Education. Published in 1986, this topic was originally proposed to the Yearbook Planning Committee of the American Council on Industrial Arts Teacher Education at the American Industrial Arts Association Conference in 1982. This was the first yearbook to focus entirely on technology education. This yearbook utilized the four organizers as identified in the Jackson's Mill Curriculum Theory, and specifically focused on the implementation of technology education at all levels, including Kindergarten through high school, and undergraduate/graduate programs (Jones & Wright, Eds., 1986).

Communication Textbooks. The inclusion of the study of communication systems into the technology education curriculum created a need for textbooks to address the content area. *Getting the Message: The Technology of Communication* (DuVall, Maughan, & Berger, 1981) began the development of textbooks focused solely on communication. The first public school textbook focusing on communication technology was *Discovering Technology: Communication* (Jones & Robb, 1986). Concurrent with its publication and Texas adoption came increased activity in the development of other communication textbooks, such as *Exploring Communications* (Seymour, Ritz, & Cloghessy, 1987). Numerous inclusions of the study of communication technology in broad-based technology education textbooks have followed.

Communication in the Curriculum

Through a review of historical and curricular influences, it has been shown that communication has readily been accepted as part of the study of technology. It is, in fact, one of the four subsystems of human technological/sociological endeavor that can be studied in isolation. Throughout history people have manufactured goods, constructed shelters, transported goods and people, and communicated ideas.

The 1960's was a time of intense activity in curriculum development for our profession. New programs were being written from Alberta, Canada to Maryland and from Detroit to Georgia, and the majority included, in some form, the study of communication. The 1970's, however, became the "turning point." In 1975 communication actually became a part of university teacher education content. The 1980's validated the inclusion of communication among the four organizers for technology education and began new thrusts in curriculum development. Public schools requested textbooks to address, specifically, the content area of communication technology, and the publishers obliged.

Communication technology is a dynamic curriculum area, full of motivational activity. Communication is an ideal situation to promote and enhance problem-solving and critical thinking skills. It is an appropriate vehicle for the inclusion of math and science applications, and to hone reading and writing skills.

An understanding of communication technology and the positive and negative impacts of communication is an integral part of developing a technologically literate population.

References

Bell, D. (1973). *The coming of post-industrial society: A venture in social forecasting*. New York: Basic Books, Inc.

Burke, J. (1978). *Connections*. Boston, MA: Little, Brown and Company.

Cochran, L. H. (1970). *Innovative programs in industrial education*. Peoria, IL: Glencoe Publishing.

DeVore, P. W. (1980). *Technology: An introduction.* Worcester, MA: Davis Publications, Inc.

DeVore, P. W., Maughan, G. R., & Griscom, W. E. (1979). Influence of technology on industrial arts matter. *Industrial arts education: Retrospect, prospect* , 28th Yearbook American Council on Industrial Arts Teacher Education, pp. 189-288.

Dibner, B. (1967). Communications. In Kranzberg, M., & Pursell, C. W. (Eds.). *Technology in western civilization, volume I.* New York: Oxford University Press.

Dugger, W. E. (1980). *Standards for industrial arts programs.* Blacksburg, VA: Virginia Polytechnic Institute and State University.

Dugger, W. E., et al. (1980). *Standards for technology education.* Reston, VA: International Technology Education Association.

DuVall, J. B., Maughan, G. R., & Berger, E. G. (1981). *Getting the message: The technology of communication.* Worcester, MA: Davis Publications, Inc.

Ereckson, T. L. & Scarborough, J. D. (1983). The "Illinois plan" and technology education. *Thresholds in education: Technology education, 9*(2) 31-32.

Hacker, M. & Listar, G. (1985). The New York state technology education program. Proceedings of Technology Education Symposium VII, *Technology Education: Issues and Trends,* (pp. 75-86). California, PA: California University of Pennsylvania.

Hales, J. A., & Snyder, J. F. (Eds.) (1981). *Jackson's Mill industrial arts curriculum theory.* Charleston, WV: West Virginia Department of Education.

Householder, D. L. (1979). Curriculum movements of the 1960's. *Industrial arts education: Retrospect, prospect,* 28th Yearbook, American Council on Industrial Arts Teacher Education, pp. 114-132.

Illinois State Board of Education. (1983). *The Illinois plan for industrial education.* Springfield, IL: Author.

Jones, R. E. (1982-83, Winter). Implementing a state plan for industrial education: A curriculum model. *Illinois Industrial Educator 2*(4), pp. 8-10.

Jones, R. E. & Robb, J. L. (1986). *Discovering technology: Communication.* Orlando, FL: Harcourt Brace Jovanovich.

Jones R. E. & Wright, J. R. (Eds.). (1986). *Implementing technology education,* 35th Yearbook, American Council on Industrial Arts Teacher Education.

Kranzberg, M. & Pursell, C. W. (Eds.). (1967). *Technology in western civilization volume 1.* New York: Oxford University Press.

Koester, D. (1983). Teutopolis high school and the Illinois plan. *Illinois Industrial Educator, 4*(3), 3-4.

Latimer, T. G. (1979). William E. Warner: His philosophy and influences upon industrial arts. *The Journal of Epsilon Pi Tau, 5*(1), 25-29.

Lauda, D. P., & McCrory, D. L. (1986). A rationale for technology education. *Implementing technology education,* 35th Yearbook, American Council on Industrial Arts Teacher Education.

Lauda, D. P., & Wright, J. R. (1983). *Eastern's technology education plan.* Charleston, IL: Eastern Illinois University.

Martin, G. E. (Ed.). (1979). *Industrial arts education: Retrospect, prospect,* 28th Yearbook, American Council on Industrial Arts Teacher Education.

Ray, W. E. (1980). Toward consensus regarding an industrial arts currciulum base. *The Journal of Epsilon Pi Tau, 6*(2), 8-12.

Seymour, R. D., Ritz, J. M., & Cloghessy, F. A. (1987). *Exploring communications*. South Holland, IL: Goodheart-Wilcox Company, Inc.

Starkweather, K. N. (1983). AIAA: Pioneering leadership in Industrial Arts/Technology Education. *Man/Society/Technology, 8*(42), 8-12.

Technical Foundation of America. (1984). *Industry and technology education: A guide for curriculum designers, implementors, and teachers.* Lansing, IL: Author.

Wright, J. R. (Ed.). (1980). *Proceedings of Symposium '80 Technology Education.* Charleston, IL: Eastern Illinois University.

Warner, W. E. (1947, April). *A curriculum to reflect technology.* Paper presented at the American Industrial Arts Convention, Columbus, OH.

Chapter 4

CONCEPTUAL MODELS FOR COMMUNICATION IN TECHNOLOGY EDUCATION PROGRAMS AT THE ELEMENTARY, MIDDLE SCHOOL, AND <u>JUNIOR HIGH SCHOOL LEVELS</u>

Donna K. Trautman
Assistant Professor
Bowling Green State University
Bowling Green, Ohio

Technology education for the elementary and middle school level has been discussed, referenced and used as a base for high school and post secondary schools for many years. It is obvious, however, that in many state curriculum guides for the elementary and middle schools, technology has not been defined to the same extent as the secondary curriculum. This chapter will: 1. review elementary and middle school technology education, 2. present sample state curriculum models, and 3. suggest different examples for implementation of communication technology curriculum for the elementary level and middle school levels.

Elementary and Middle School Technology Education

"Because of the important relationship which exists between culture and technology, the elementary school that prepares students to understand and live successfully within their culture must include technology-based content" (Peterson, 1986, p. 47). Children as well as adults live in a technological society and use the products of technology every day. The importance of the understanding of technology in our society is apparent and need not be rationalized as an important aspect of our school curriculum. However, the appropriate timing of the introduction to technology as subject matter is of concern in the literature. Peterson (1986) believed that "the elementary school level is where the development of an essential understanding of technology should begin" (p. 47).

DeVore (1980) pointed out that "individual perceptions of various topics or phenomena are largely dependent on a person's background, the amount of study and reflection given to the topic and personal experiences with the phenomena" (p. 42). If this is true, an individual that does not receive the exposure to technology in a systematic manner may not be able to develop a well-informed perception of the technology that affects one's life. "The aim of the elementary school technology education program is to develop a first-hand understanding of the technology that supports daily life" (Peterson, 1986, p. 47). The goals of an elementary technology education program must be formed to provide direction to the development of a program to help children understand technology.

It is at the elementary and middle school levels that the goals and objectives of technology education can begin to be promoted. The major concern of curriculum developers is to provide appropriate information and activities for the developmental level of the students. Sequencing the content according to the age of the student, especially in the elementary and middle schools where the levels of development of each student change very fast, is as important as the integration of all subject areas in technology education. The sequence of information and activities must be coordinated with abilities of the children. Technology education at the elementary and middle school levels is very complex and very critical to accomplishing the goals of the field.

Elementary and Middle School Technology Education

Communication technology is an integral aspect of the study of technology and the elementary and middle schools provide the appropriate atmosphere for its awareness and exploration. Several state plans for technology education have been reviewed and identify their preferences for the sequencing and content of technology and communication technology. Although the plans are quite comprehensive for secondary education, the plans are brief in their explanation for the elementary and middle schools.

The scope and sequence for the *West Virginia Plan for Technology Education* (1987) mandates awareness, integrated technology, for grades K - 4 (see Figure 4.1). It also identifies exploration, in the areas of communication, construction, manufacturing and transportation, for grades 5 - 8. There are no general goals of technology education in the plan that target elementary or middle school technology education, however the goals presented in the document provide an important direction for primary grade technology educators to follow.

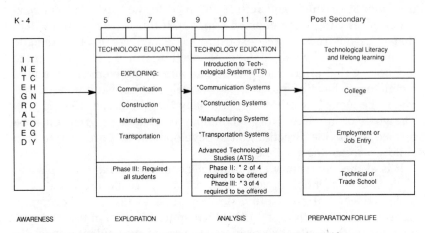

Scope and Sequence

| K - 4 | 5 6 7 8 | 9 10 11 12 | Post Secondary |

Figure 4.1: **West Virginia Plan for Technology Education.**

The *Technology Education in Pennsylvania Program Guide* (1988, p. 7) identifies that at the elementary level (K - 5 or 6) "technology education activities are integrated in the general elementary school program for understanding how people communicate, transport, manufacture, construct and use energy." Pennsylvania sequences broad introductory laboratory experiences in communication, power/transportation, and manufacturing/construction. In 1983, Pennsylvania produced an *Elementary School Industrial Arts Educator's Handbook* which provided approaches for "Making the Elementary Education Curriculum More Effective Through Industrial Arts Activities" (Lucy, et al., cover). This comprehensive guide takes into consideration not only the content of teaching technology but also the developmental levels of the child.

Missouri's Industrial Technology Education Guide (1987) recommends awareness of technology through infusing activities into the regular ongoing elementary school curriculum (Level I). Level II, grades 6 - 9, builds an understanding of technology and "must involve a systematic overview of the most important tools, machines, materials and processes of industrial technology. This course must sample the key elements of each technological cluster and it must not focus on any single cluster" (1987, p. 3).

A Model for Technology Education in Ohio (1989) looks at technology in the primary grades as " a vehicle for illustrating the interrelatedness of the typical core topics of math, science, language arts, social studies, movement, and the arts" (p. 8). Ohio's model explains that this integration should be delivered on the levels of awareness, demonstration and participation (see Figure 4.2). Technology education in the middle grades in Ohio's model continue exploration and integration and focus activities on systems, resources, problems, solutions, history and development.

Technology Education - Elementary Grades

Systems Operations	Current Operations	Environment	History

Technology Education - Middle Grades

Systems	Resources	Problems	Solutions	History	Development

Technology Systems - Secondary Grades

Small Program	Medium Program	Large Program	Other Suggested Courses

| Grades 9 - 10 Communication Technology Systems Physical Technology Systems Bio-Related Technology Systems | Grades 9 - 10 Communication Technology Systems Physical Technology Systems Bio-Related Technology Systems Ergonomics Computer Applications in Technology Construction Systems Manufacturing Systems | Grades 9 - 10 Communication Technology Systems Physical Technology Systems Bio-Related Technology Systems Ergonomics Computer Applications in Technology Construction Systems Manufacturing Systems Global Technology Communication Networks Energy/Power/Transportation Systems | Electronic Communication Systems Graphic Communication Systems Construction Planning and Design Electro/Mechanical Systems Product Design for Manufacturing Manufacturing Production Systems |
| Grades 11 - 12 Technology in Society | Grades 11 - 12 Technology in Society Special Problems in Technology | Grades 11 - 12 Technology in Society Special Problems in Technology Principles of Technology Pre-Engineering | Leadership development through participation in local chapter and statewide activities of the Technology Student Association, Grades 7 - 12. |

Technology Education - Post Secondary Grades

Technology in Culture	Technology in the Liberal Arts

Technology Education - Adult and Continuing Education

Consumer	Career	Leisure	General Knowledge

Figure 4.2: Ohio's program structure.

It is evident from a sample of state plans for technology education that the focus of the elementary programs have been planned to take the integrated approach with the other general education subjects. A method for the integration and dissemination of technology education needs to be developed that includes the other aspects of a child's education.

Communication Technology in the Curriculum

The four state models presented for technology education provide some interesting approaches for the elementary and middle school curriculum. It is clear that the history of technology provides students with the base knowledge to experiment, explore and become aware of their surroundings. But we have the challenge to not only help students to become productive citizens, but to prepare them to function and contribute in tomorrow's society.

Although few of these state models directly refer to communication technology in the elementary school, it is assumed that it is a part of the integrated approach of teaching technology in a systematic manner. For a classroom teacher to infuse technology into the typical elementary or middle school curriculum, specific lessons and activities must be planned. Communication technology provides an excellent vehicle to integrate not only the "other" traditional areas of study but to combine all other areas within technology. If a teacher is to integrate technology into the classroom, how can communication technology be integrated into other subject areas, where should it happen, and what is the most effective way to teach? These are some questions that are overlooked many times in the elementary and middle schools.

It has already been noted that understanding the physical and emotional development of children is very complex, however the developmental levels of the elementary and middle school children cannot be ignored when developing lessons and activities. There is a vast difference between a first and a fifth grade student and a sixth and an eighth grade student. However, there is no reason that the study of communication systems cannot be introduced and understood at the first grade level. With appropriate vocabulary lists, reading assignments, social studies, and math skills, young creative and imaginative minds can be guided through lecture and activity to become aware of and experiment with communication technologies. The goal is to make these students aware of communication systems and technology and provide them a base of information for problem solving in the future. Just as we progress in reading, math, etc., elementary and middle school students can progress in learning about and have experiences with communication technology. As curriculum developers and classroom teachers lectures and activities need to be adapted to the developmental level of the child.

The integration of communication technology into the elementary classroom can happen in many different ways. One way may just be to make a concerted effort to point out communication systems used within the regular day-to-day lectures and activities. The students may be required to identify different methods of communication and types of communication technology as the year progresses. This sounds like the easiest method for the teacher, however to provide the information in a systematic manner is very difficult.

Every lesson plan that a teacher uses must reflect the communication systems, devices, careers, etc. that are associated with that lesson. Important connections may not be clear to the children and the purpose of studying the topic may be lost if lessons are not well planned. Activities should be used to demonstrate and illustrate difficult concepts. An example of a social studies lesson about the American Indians and the methods of communication used within their tribes and with other tribes could explore interesting associations about the different types of communication methods used today which were derived from American Indians. Figure 4.3 shows a common lesson plan format and a small change that can be made to help the teacher remember to add communication information to the lesson.

Title:
Grade Level:

Purpose of Activity: *(Is this an integrated activity or lesson?)*

Objectives of the lesson:

Special Communication Objectives:

Materials/tools Needed: *(Are these materials/tools "real" and/or modified for the age of the child?)*

Special Safety Precautions:

Procedures:

Outcomes: *(Is there anything that can be sent to newspapers, displays made from or that can be sent home to parents?)*

Evaluation: *(Does the evaluation include career awareness or whether application of learned theories transpired?)*

Figure 4.3: Elementary or middle school lesson plan.

Another way a teacher might consider infusing the study of communication into an elementary or middle school curriculum is to designate a time period to teach about technology. During this time, reading assignments, spelling lists, math problems, writing, social studies, etc. can be integrated. A portion of the required time for each of these subjects per week is easily justified in this structured approach.

A "technology hour" may be planned to have a portion of an hour reserved for discussion/lecture (see Figure 4.4). A major effort to connect communication technology and communication systems into the child's world as it is today and will be in the future should be presented during the discussion/lecture. The remaining part of the hour would be for activity, an important aspect of this teaching method. An example, a fifth grade class might have a communication activity which could be experienced over a period of weeks and involve career education, reading, writing, spelling, social studies, current events and math. The children would write, create, research, set-up, and produce their own news show for and about their school. The possibilities for the students to learn and synthesize in this exercise are endless. This activity can be used in any of the grades K-8 with appropriate planning.

The "technology hour" becomes an appropriate time to "allow" students to synthesize and apply this knowledge in a meaningful activity. It is important whenever possible to use "real" equipment or devices for all ages of students during these activities. The process is very important, however without the product for them to correlate with what they observe daily or use at home, the "technology hour" approach may be less effective.

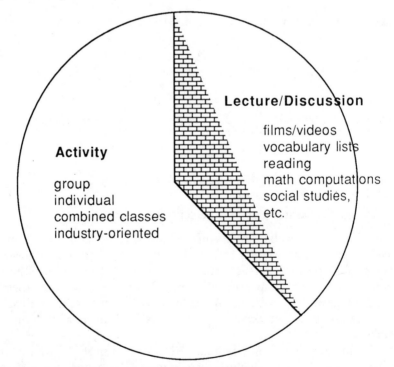

Figure 4.4: "Technology Hour" time division.

A business and/or industry approach to communication technology may be appropriate for a specific school district with strong support from the community. "Adopt a school" programs are excellent ways to involve business and industry in the classroom. They can provide resources, people, enthusiasm and perhaps a place for field exploration. Government agencies as well as large corporations are a resource for teaching communication technology. Educators must remember that including a person unfamiliar with the classroom setting will take some planning and preparation time. A class data sheet may also be an aid for a guest speaker or sponsoring company. Figure 4.5 is an example of a data sheet that may be developed. The key to this approach is to have regular contact with the company.

School _____

Grade Level _____ Room Number _____

Teacher _____

Contact phone number _____

Number of Students _____ Age Range of Students _____

Overall atmosphere in classroom _____

_____

_____

Special way to get students attention? (ie. raise right hand, turn out lights, etc.)

_____

Policy on treats _____

_____

_____

Room available for demonstration _____

_____

Special Instructions _____

_____

_____

Figure 4.5: Elementary or middle school class data sheet.

At the middle school level a quarter or semester course may be to set up an in-class business or company to take an industry approach to solving a communication problem and might involve career exploration, reading, spelling, social studies, math, and science. While a product may be produced, the process involved is the key to the activity. The students would experience how business/industry solves technological problems to meet human needs. A local business group or chamber of commerce would be an appropriate place to begin looking for a sponsor for the class activity. A special note to parents may also locate a company that may be willing to lend support.

A more social approach to teaching communication technology for either the elementary or middle school level may help students learn about the communication systems in their world by studying social problems using a systems model. The systems approach, as discussed by Maley (1989), provided four steps:

1. Communicate the nature, qualities and components of a system.
2. Students identify systems that may be found.
3. Research, construction, and graphics carried out by individuals or pairs of students.
4. Sharing and reporting of what has been learned.

This approach allows a student to identify systems and subsystems of the communication available to them in one's city, state, country and in the world. The identification of television, telephone, radio, emergency communication, newspaper, etc. provide the students with the knowledge of "what is." The teacher can proceed further in the classroom to ask "what if" and to problem solve potential future communication problems.

An example of an activity that could be adapted to any age level is called "Our City." A planned approach to building a model city applies all the areas involved in technology education. This method of integrating technology education could be planned for a year long or a semester activity at the middle school level. The degree to which the city is developed is controlled by the teacher and determined by the age of the students. All of the components of a successful city can be researched by different students, reported, and placed in the model city. Initial planning for the layout of the city is necessary; however, the extent of the plans depends on the students. The components could be as simple as telephone or cable television lines available in a city. Buildings are designed, signs are printed and placed in areas of traffic flow. Career lists could be made identifying the communication related positions and people required to make a city function. The outcomes of this type of activity can be very beneficial to all areas of a child's education.

There are numerous ways to integrate the study of communication technology into the elementary and middle school curriculum. Perhaps the most important decision the teacher has to make is which of the methods of implementation are most appropriate for their classroom, their specific style and teaching environment.

Teaching Environment

The "where" of teaching communication technology is really incidental. The teacher should be able to take the children to appropriate places where they may use communication systems and devices. The availability of video recorders, computers, and books allows the teacher to bring information and experiences to the student. Integrated activities should be able to be completed in the classroom with perhaps some rearrangement of furniture.

The elementary or middle school teacher may keep a display of current communication technology or the transition from traditional to future technology in the classroom for observation and interaction. This may provide students with some "directed thinking" incentive. A display also allows visitors to see how communication technology is being presented in the curriculum. It seems as if it would be the best circumstance if a teacher had a special room to teach technology, however at the elementary level it is probably not necessary. At the middle school level a place where long term activities could be staged is essential. While traditional industrial equipment is no longer needed for the study of communication technology, an environment dedicated to the study of technology will assist the teacher in maintaining continuity throughout the instructional period.

The library in an elementary and middle school is a very important place for children. The library is a place of value and technology teachers should use this excellent resource. Perhaps a "technology corner" in the library could feature books related to communication careers, inventions and innovations, history, and video tapes on technology (or other media related to communication technology). The students start to identify communication technology in all aspects of their school work. If a "technology corner" is not feasible, perhaps a featured list of books distributed monthly by the librarian or the teacher could be presented to the students and their parents. These lists of books may be theme oriented according to communication events, innovations or people related to that particular month.

Outside Support

Advertising communication technology activities to parents and the community may be the most valuable tool a technology teacher has. It is important that parents and the community think of technology as a subject that integrates. Support from parents could yield their assistance in the classroom, providing supplies and recognition by the school board or PTA. Many of the schools across the country have faced financial difficulty and have had to face the possibility of cutting certain activities. However, those activities which had the community's and parents' support are often spared or may receive outside assistance. Communication technology teachers need to illustrate the importance of the subject matter not only to the principal and other administrators, but to the community.

Communication In Technology Education In the Future

The elementary and middle school technology teachers have two important roles that will influence the child's future. The first, is to provide a strong base to recognize, practice and evaluate communication technology in a systematic manner. The second is to provide a problem solving base and an unrestricted creative atmosphere. It is important to stress that we use products of technology to solve problems and it is important that they are ready to apply their knowledge to solve future problems.

At these formative levels of education students begin to learn about the social, cultural, and technological world. They can begin to observe and integrate how all subjects are related through a multi- and inter-disciplinary approach to teaching about technology. As a part of technology education they should experience solving technological problems which face society (these could be social or environmental) and study the impacts that changing communication systems will have upon their lives.

The elementary and middle schools provide the early experiences which enable children to develop future interests and as such provides the foundation on which the subsequent study of technology occurs. All schools are challenged to contribute to the technological literacy of children by providing the study of communication technology as a part of technology education at all levels.

References

DeVore, P. W. (1980). *Technology: An introduction*. Worcester, MA: Davis Publications, Inc.

Lucy, J. H. (1983). *Elementary school industrial arts*. Harrisburg, PA: Pennsylvania Department of Education.

Missouri State Board of Education. (1987). *Missouri industrial technology education guide*. Columbia, MO: Missouri State Board of Education.

Maley, D. (March, 1989). Paper presented to the International Technology Education Association, Dallas, Texas.

Pennsylvania Department of Education. (1988). *Technology education in Pennsylvania*. Harrisburg, PA: Pennsylvania Department of Education.

Peterson, R. E. (1986). Elementary school technology education programs. In Jones, R. E. & Wright J. R. (Eds.), *Implementing technology education* (pp. 47-69), Peoria, IL: American Council on Industrial Arts Teacher Education.

West Virginia Board of Education. (1987). *West Virginia industrial arts/ technology education*. Ripley, WV: The West Virginia Board of Education.

Ohio Department of Education. (1989). *A model for technology education in Ohio*. Columbus, OH: Ohio Department of Education.

Chapter 5

CONCEPTUAL MODELS FOR COMMUNICATION IN TECHNOLOGY EDUCATION PROGRAMS AT THE HIGH SCHOOL LEVEL

Richard D. Seymour
Assistant Professor
Department of Industry and Technology
Ball State University
Muncie, Indiana

Introduction

For young adults, high school brings a variety of new interests, friends, opportunities, and aspirations. Students mature and develop their own unique personalities during their secondary school experiences. And, they usually find that numerous forms of communication become vitally important to social and personal success. Radio and television programming provides hours of information and entertainment. The telephone becomes a close friend. Calculators, typewriters, and computers are needed to complete school assignments. During this period, the ability to read road maps and understand traffic signals becomes necessary. Interest in popular music and feature movies usually increases. In addition, the marketing tactics of various companies often bring about significant changes in buying habits.

The secondary school experience represents the last free public education for youngsters in preparation for a lifetime in a dynamic society. It is designed to build upon lessons learned during grades K-6. As Boyer notes, it should "extend and broaden the perspective of every student" (1983, p. 94). New and more difficult coursework should also "provide students with an in-depth foundation for career preparation" (ITEA, 1988, p. 19). Many teenagers will plan to take the job and personal skills learned in high school directly into the labor force. For others, high school helps launch them into a degree program at a small college or major university. Perhaps most importantly,

Lauda suggests that students "leave the public schools with the desire and intent to gain new knowledge and skills the rest of their lives" (Kemp & Schwaller, 1988, p. 12).

The ability to work and live in a modern information age is becoming increasingly dependent on the efficient utilization of communication technologies. Devices such as telephones, photocopiers, computers, and facsimile machines assist our business activities. Stereo systems, VCRs, and microcomputers are now common household items. Cellular telephone service, electronic banking, satellite navigation, and cable television networks are found in most regions. Unfortunately, too many of us take these devices, systems, networks, and media for granted. When describing our current dependence on communication technology, Adamson notes how it is "relied upon by all but understood by few" (1988, p. 37).

A major challenge in today's secondary schools is to prepare students to be technologically literate; to, in fact, understand how technology shapes and controls this complex world. Unfortunately, most high school seniors would have difficulty describing even the most basic communication technologies. For example, they would probably have trouble explaining how cable TV pictures arrive at their homes, or how their money travels along an electronic funds transfer network. Other students have little idea how audio cassettes, radio programs, and motion pictures are produced. Today, most schools fail to provide an educational program which allows students to learn about even the most fundamental communication technologies.

The previous chapter described several ways to incorporate introductory-level communication topics into the middle school curriculum. This section will suggest the means for expanding upon those basic concepts. Coursework available at the secondary school level should build on content covered in previous classes. By taking additional classes related to communication systems, students should be able to explore information technologies in greater depth. More importantly, the instructor will have the unique opportunity to go beyond the "black box" level and concentrate on specific technical systems, such as visual, audio, and audio-visual technologies.

Modern high school communication programs may also feature a direct link among related school subjects. Zuga describes the interdisciplinary study of technology as an "attempt to integrate the knowledge of other disciplines" (Kemp & Schwaller, p. 61). A quick review of any secondary school class schedule will show that over 50 percent of available courses deal with some form of human communication (e.g., band, theater, journalism, typing, public speaking, English, art, etc.). Yet, few focus on the "technical means" or a systems approach to how these interrelate or function. An interdisciplinary look at typical networks permits secondary students to understand better the operation and influence of today's communication systems.

Finally, a secondary study of information systems should reveal a fascinating world of rapidly emerging technologies. Although most classroom assignments and "hands-on" activities may focus on basic concepts, these courses should also address the latest in communication systems. Topics included in advanced courses should help introduce the communication technologies of the future. This is only achieved by constantly updating content, lessons, and activities to reflect the most recent devices and systems.

Communication Systems at the Secondary Level

Since the 1940's, scholars have attempted to explain the communication process through various models, formulas, and diagrams. It was about this time in history when film, radio, and television first gained prominence on the American scene, and communication scientists were eager to study these new technologies (Rogers, 1986). Among the most popular theories of this period was the work published by Claude E. Shannon and Warren Weaver in 1949, entitled *The Mathematical Theory of Communication.* Shannon (an electrical engineer at Bell Labs) and Weaver (of the Rockefeller Foundation) proposed a linear model of communication that has since gained wide acceptance (see Figure 5.1). Variations of this model are often used to help organize a conceptual framework for the study of communication technology at the secondary school level.

In practice, this simple model has evolved into the basis for a systems approach to the study of information technologies. As Jones (1988) observes, when applying this instructional approach, "the resources used in communication, the technical processes in communication, the industrial application (the relationships between communication and the other systems), and the technological impact of communication can also be studied" (Kemp & Schwaller, p. 103). Using visual systems as an example, the illustration in Figure 5.2 shows the sample topics that might be included in a graphic communication program.

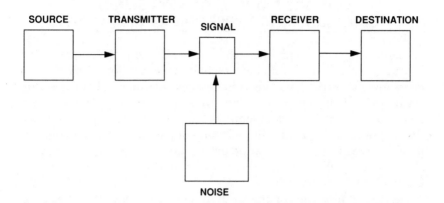

Figure 5.1: The communication process, as defined by Shannon and Weaver in *The Mathematical Theory of Communication*, is useful in developing program models in communication technology programs.

Throughout the rest of this chapter, you will learn of several means for organizing communication content into secondary courses of varying length and focus. Sample program structures will be presented and suggestions noted for the implementation of these models. Emphasis will be placed on creating an integrated program which addresses all types of media and systems. Finally, trends in the study of communication systems will be covered with implications for future program development.

A Model of the Graphic Communication Process

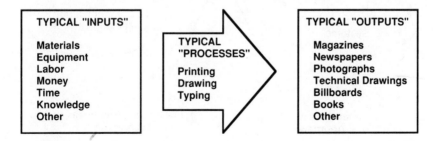

Figure 5.2: The application of a "systems approach" to the study of modern communication technology.

Content Models for High School
Communication Technology Programs

Among the first (and often the most difficult) challenges to an instructor establishing a modern technology education program is in developing a curricular model for the new instructional system. Program models help explain the sequence and relationships of topics in a given curriculum. A model identifies the major content organizers for the program. It also guides the selection of (a) individual course titles, (b) objectives and goals, (c) anticipated outcomes, (d) an overview of class content, (e) concepts to be covered, and (f) related elements in the total instructional plan.

The use of a model for the study of communication technology is vitally important to the integrity and success of the secondary program. After all, "our technology has become so sophisticated . . . that it is no longer possible for any one person to know all about any broad area of technology" (DuVall, Maughan, & Berger, 1981, p. 3). Ultimately, the content should be structured into manageable courses and/or units in specific classes. But the overall "theme" for the program is reflected in the way content is divided among various classes.

Figure 5.3: Different means of organizing content in a secondary school communication program.

There are numerous means of organizing content for a communication technology program. The more common models are: (a) the study of the basic human/technological systems, (b) mass communication media or ventures, (c) interdisciplinary approaches and (d) information-processing activities. The remainder of this section expands on these four methods of structuring content in communication technology (see Figure 5.3).

The Study of Human/Technological Systems

The exchange of ideas, feelings, and information has been an important human activity since the earliest recorded times. We generally send and receive information using one of our five senses: touch, feel, hearing, sight, and taste. However, most personal communication involves a direct exchange of messages by talking or gesturing. The dominant senses involve our ability to see and hear; over ninety percent of what we learn is gained via these channels. This is an important consideration in the development of a study of modern communication systems.

At the same time, communication technology can be viewed in terms of extending the human sensory system. Most technical devices serve as a direct means of increasing our human capabilities. For example, we can only talk to another person when they're within shouting range. But with a telephone or radio, we have the ability to talk around the globe. Similar telecommunications systems allow us to link machines and even entire societies. Again, most communication technologies are designed to allow us to extend beyond our natural limitations.

Combining the ideas of (a) using technical means to (b) extend our human capabilities of sight and hearing, one can readily see the justification for structuring communication programs around common visual or audio/audio-visual techniques (Jones & Robb, 1986, p. 22). Topics related to visual media are frequently covered in secondary courses related to graphic communication. In a similar manner, systems based on our audio and audio-visual senses are usually addressed in courses which cover the electronic media. This coursework may include the familiar activities of broadcasting, telecommunications, hard-wired systems, and data processing (Wright & Sterry, 1983). Therefore, one functional model for a high school communication technology program would be to divide the content quality equally among the graphic and electronic media, as shown in Figure 5.4.

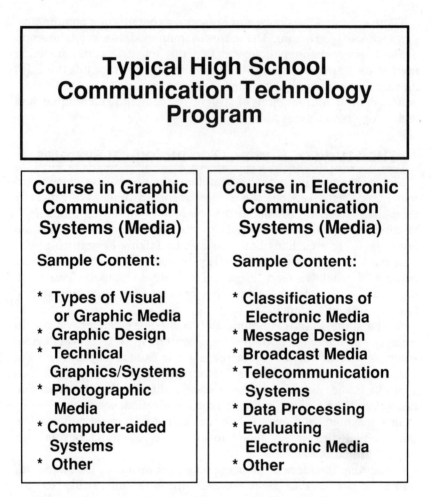

Typical High School Communication Technology Program

Course in Graphic Communication Systems (Media)	Course in Electronic Communication Systems (Media)
Sample Content:	Sample Content:
* Types of Visual or Graphic Media * Graphic Design * Technical Graphics/Systems * Photographic Media * Computer-aided Systems * Other	* Classifications of Electronic Media * Message Design * Broadcast Media * Telecommunication Systems * Data Processing * Evaluating Electronic Media * Other

Figure 5.4: An example of organizing course content by the two major human/technological systems of communication.

Coursework in Visual (Graphic) Communication Systems

In modern society, the work of many individuals is visually oriented. Artists, drafters, writers, architects, secretaries, and advertising personnel must be especially gifted when it comes to producing graphic materials that "get a message across" to varying audiences. They are among millions who plan and reproduce graphic media on a daily basis. The ability to communicate with visual images is a fundamental and important trait. The prime instructional purpose behind many school activities is to enhance one's ability to develop visual media.

In a contemporary technology-based program, students should have an opportunity to learn about and improve their ability to utilize graphic communication systems. This includes the chance to design, produce, and measure the results of graphic media. Obviously, students would be introduced to the basic concepts of visual technologies at the junior high level, so content covered in these advanced courses would build on previously learned topics.

Utilizing a systems approach to organize the content for a class in graphic communications often proves to be both convenient and useful (again, note the simplicity of the model shown in Figure 5.2). Course objectives should also follow this format to maintain consistency. If applying these criteria to a course in visual communication, one can easily identify major topics. For example, the system "inputs" would include topics related to design and preproduction activities. Designing visual messages might involve learning about audience assessment, reviewing elements of graphic layout, and covering the importance of message placement. Preproduction techniques typically include image generation and the preparation of image carriers and/or a transfer medium. Electronic or computer aided composition, development of comprehensives, and preparing final mechanicals would be covered in this part of the curriculum. Other sample topics might include the planning of technical illustrations, development of detailed sketches, and the elements of product and structural design.

The "processing" of graphic media involves numerous reproduction, computerized, and photographic techniques. Perhaps the most familiar involves the printing of graphic messages using one of the common methods of reproduction (relief, screen, lithographic, gravure, electrostatic, and various specialty processes). Related subject matter might include line and continuous tone photography, cinematography, and similar related technologies. Certainly the area of computer graphics, and related areas of typesetting, data processing, and desktop publishing (DTP) would be addressed under processing of information.

The better communication programs address each of these technologies in some manner. Typical instruction involves formal lectures, field trips, the use of movies or related media, and numerous hands-on laboratory assignments of a problem-solving nature.

A student in a graphic communication course should spend the majority of class time composing and producing materials which involve graphic techniques and learn about the technologies which are applied through these processes. This exposure to various processes should allow the student to compare the value of each method and, thus, be better prepared to select the best process for future graphic needs. In theory, the "process" is directly associated to available inputs (time, money, etc.) and desired outcomes (quantity, color, and physical use).

The "outputs" of graphic communication efforts vary tremendously. Skill in producing visual materials may be applied to develop road maps, architectural plans, computer graphics, bumper stickers, billboards, packaging, textbook covers, and slides for business presentations. Yet, many of the production techniques for creating individual media are related. The implications for the communication teacher are that a seemingly unlimited number of instructional activities can be developed that will illustrate the most fundamental concepts of graphic media.

A modern graphic communication program could also include a unit or module which would cover the evaluation of visual media. Designers of communication materials often rate the success of their media on the ability to communicate the desired message. This includes more than the commercial appeal of the developed media; the designer is interested in the impact of the final product. A secondary school communication program should cover message placement as related to varying audiences, financial considerations, aesthetics, and content.

Finally, the graphic communication sequence could include topics which extend well beyond the efforts of the printing industry. Many visual materials involve related applications, but they are quite different in nature. For example, graphic designers create items such as logos, letterheads, annual reports, technical illustrations, packaging, maps, TV graphics, and floor plans (Berryman, 1979). This listing helps illustrate the diversity in this area of communication. As teachers build their secondary programs, they may select several of these items as the focus of laboratory activities.

Courses in graphic communication systems will help the student better understand the importance, development, and use of visual media. The majority of class time is structured to allow for hands-on assignments. Yet, these classes are not to be confused with a printing or graphic arts course. Wright and Sterry observe that these courses introduce "the traditional areas of printing and photography, but suggest a somewhat broader view" (1983, p. 27). The instructor is challenged to apply both experience and insight to produce a course which addresses the needs of the student. This means covering as many topics within communication as possible within the limits of the school's resources.

Coursework in Electronic Communication Systems

Perhaps the most exciting technical developments this century have been in the technologies related to electronic media. Home computers, fiber optics, digital stereos, and cellular telephones head a list of topics once considered pure fiction. Now electronic communication systems "have restructured the nature of business, industry, and the family" (Dordick, 1986, p. 20). Furthermore, the trend to automate and computerize many common daily tasks means this area will continue to grow in importance.

Today's secondary school students already recognize the impact of communication technologies in their daily lives. From radio or TV newscasts in the morning to computers at school to feature movies on cable TV at night, numerous electronic systems and devices have invaded their daily routines. But they often fail to realize how communication technologies have "enabled people to interact in a timely fashion on a global level in social, political, economic, and scientific areas" (Cannon & Luecke, 1984, p. 22). Teenagers typically benefit from the convenience of these devices and networks without a conceptual understanding of basic telecommunication and computer systems. Of course, we are reminded that "a technologically literate person would have knowledge about and understanding" of basic technical systems (ITEA, 1985, p. 10).

The basis of today's electronic media is the use of "electrical energy to transmit the information to be communicated" (Cannon & Luecke, 1984, p. 20). More specifically, the foundational concept is the "utilization of some segment of the electromagnetic spectrum" in the development and transmission of messages (Seymour, 1987, p. 43). In structuring a course in electronic communication systems, it is necessary to review the application of various signals along the electromagnetic spectrum (see Figure 5.5). Quite often, the most distinguishing characteristic of various audio and audio-visual systems is the nature of the transmission frequencies.

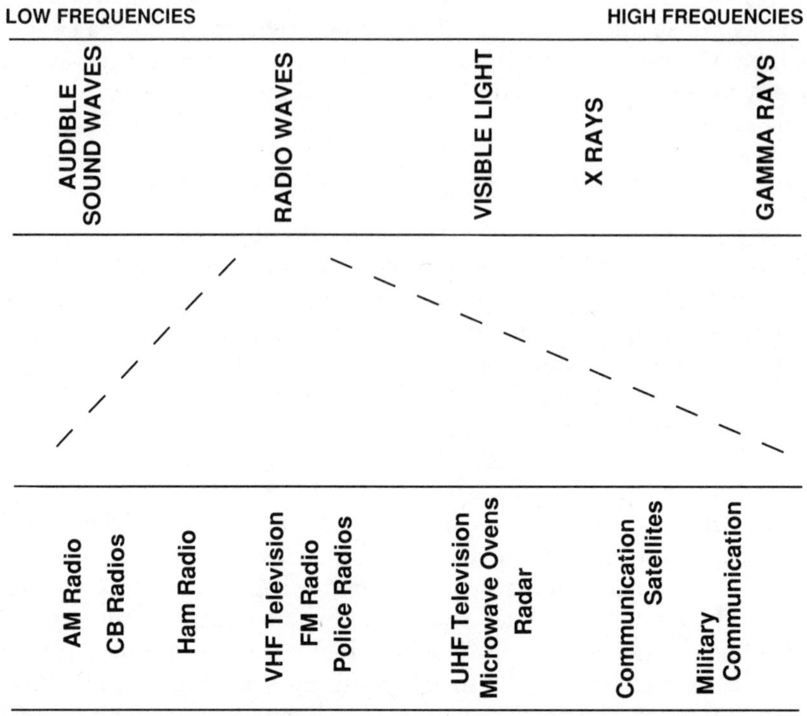

LOW FREQUENCIES   HIGH FREQUENCIES

AUDIBLE SOUND WAVES	RADIO WAVES	VISIBLE LIGHT	X RAYS	GAMMA RAYS

AM Radio CB Radios Ham Radio VHF Television FM Radio Police Radios UHF Television Microwave Ovens Radar Communication Satellites Military Communication

Figure 5.5: Courses in electronic communication media are usually based on the application of the electromagnetic spectrum in modern technological systems.

One method for structuring this type of course would be to apply a systems approach; that is, to review the major inputs, processes, and outputs common of various media and systems. Hendricks and Sterry suggest that the "inputs" of communication systems (people, materials, information, capital, etc.) are used to get a "message ready for transmission" (1987, p. 18). In terms of electronic media, this includes organizing the key resources to plan and produce various messages. Therefore, the electronic communication course would involve design activities such as storyboarding, computer programming, script writing, and related tasks. In addition, audience assessment activities are covered at this time. Other sample topics include set design, rehearsal for cast and crew, program debugging, and/or system testing. All the major development activities of electronic devices, systems, or media would be included in this phase of the course.

The "processing" of electronic messages involves the transmission of information "in many forms: radio signals, computer languages, audible (or acoustical) energy, waves of invisible light, etc." (Seymour, 1987, p. 43). In terms of commercial and private radio operations, broadcast frequencies are assigned to individual citizens and companies. Data processing involves various software packages used to manipulate text and graphics. Radar and microwave relay systems involve very high energy waveforms. Modern compact disk players and fiber optic networks have evolved from applying laser (light) technologies. In theory, students should become familiar with each of the numerous types of signals used in electronic communication.

Perhaps it would be appropriate to mention that two of the more popular laboratory activities in electronic communication courses involve (a) videotaping short features, and (b) learning to operate microcomputer systems. A contemporary program will address modern information technologies and permit students to use a variety of equipment and production practices. The development of video productions and computer programs are two means of addressing these important technologies. However, these activities should not preclude the program's goals of covering the entire realm of electronic media. Boyer warns us of the "current inclination to equate technology with computers" (1983, p. 111). In other words, the "process" (broadcasting, data processing, etc.) should remain the focus of the course, not the equipment.

Finally, a complete study of electronic communication media involves the "outputs" of the production and/or transmission efforts. It is easy to neglect the many products and services which result from the successful delivery of electronic signals and media. The "outputs" of electronic systems range from radio broadcasts to receiving FAX (facsimile) documents to decoding a ham radio transmission sent in Morse Code. Quite often, it involves assessing whether or not the message was clearly received. The appropriateness and efficiency of the entire system could also be evaluated.

The Study of Communication Industries, Media, and Ventures

A challenge of technology-based courses is to help young adults "understand technological innovation, the productivity of technology, and the impact of technology on the quality of life" (ITEA, 1988, p. 16). Typically, this theme has been most evident in manufacturing enterprise classes or units when students form and operate a mock company. The value of this approach is that students can readily see how resources (materials, money, their own skills and talents, etc.) are organized and managed for greatest output (both in financial and in qualitative terms). Similar instructional activities in the communication cluster would include implementing activities that mirror the development of mass communication products and services.

In a technological world, information (knowledge) represents the most precious resource in any modern venture. Combining creative ideas with technical knowledge, capital, and other resources allows us to produce many unique items and services. Among the familiar outputs of communication firms are movies, newspapers, textbooks, radio programs, and computer software. At the center of today's information society are millions of individuals who profit from the generation, development, processing, transmission, and storage of information. In their daily efforts as managers and workers in information industries, they account for the majority of the active workforce. Several of the more familiar commercial ventures include publishing, filmmaking, data processing, recording, telecommunications, and the broadcast services. Individuals and enterprises which specialize in the application of mass communication technologies now dominate our economy.

The concept of mass communication is important in modern society. At times, we wish to link "one or a few individuals to . . . an audience of many" (Rogers, 1986, p. 2). The basic decision involves selecting the best technology to get the desired message to a large, and often diverse, audience. Knowledge of the benefits and disadvantages of various systems, media, and technologies is needed to make intelligent choices.

The study of communication systems at the secondary level can be structured to parallel the activities and ventures of information industries. This advanced coursework allows students to learn the concepts of management, business organization, and production as related to communication technologies. We often fail to recognize the complex production effort required to complete feature movies, television programs, cassette tapes, instructional software, newspapers, or various print media. Perhaps more significantly, students will learn in these courses that the degree of success in modern communication is often determined by whether a profit is realized from the exchange of ideas or messages.

Therefore, a comprehensive method of structuring a secondary-level communication program is to focus on the organization, management, and operation of typical information industries. To accentuate the ventures that have the greatest societal impact, systems and media related to mass communication firms are usually identified for this type of program (see Figure 5.6). Further, a course title such as "Mass Communication" is recommended over more restrictive labels (which imply the focus of the course is solely on desktop publishing, telecommunications, data processing, etc.).

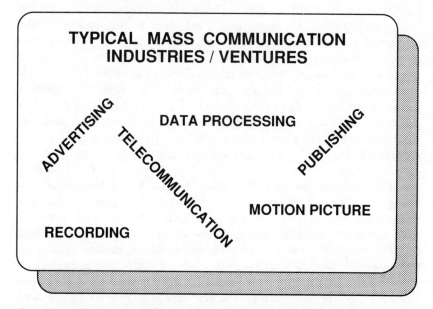

Figure 5.6: Examples of various communication industries.

Coursework related to mass communication may address a wide range of topics. For example, one objective would be to study the innovative efforts of modern companies as they strive to develop new products or services. Students might be given sample design assignments that simulate the creative tasks of a scriptwriter, software developer, or advertising executive. Another developmental activity might be to challenge the students to adapt an emerging technology (fiber optics, ink jet printing, etc.) to solve a known communication problem. Numerous laboratory activities which require the students apply their previous experience and creative talents may be implemented throughout this type of course.

A second course objective might be to address the controls imposed on mass communication media and systems. Social and governmental regulations are fairly strict in most commercial ventures. Examples of regulatory efforts include rating movies (G, PG, PG-13, R, and X), the issuance of broadcast standards, and the licensing of radio and television stations (so identified by station call letters and specific frequencies). The related issues include the need to copyright videotaped programming, software, and printed materials; attempts to maintain industrial standards in the production and transmission of various media; and penalties for violating laws and regulations.

A major theme of a mass communication course would be the economic aspects involved with operating a modern venture. The means of financing and marketing various products or services are commonly reviewed. Students might discover how key individuals often earn millions of dollars from producing television shows or feature films, designing new software, or anchoring a national news program. Class activities might also reveal the means of profiting from the distribution of cable television programs, of producing record albums, or by selling advertising space in magazines and on billboards.

A mass communication course might involve a variety of individual and group activities which develop advanced research and development skills. Guest speakers might be invited to describe how they have applied new technologies. Potential careers may be discovered through exciting conversations with broadcasters, managers at satellite downlink facilities, publishers, and computer specialists. Field trips to local communication industries or businesses support such classroom instruction. Perhaps the best means of addressing the practices of mass communication firms is through a simulated classroom enterprise.

Organizing a mass communication enterprise allows secondary students to learn firsthand about production, programming, design, development, and similar communication techniques. Stated another way, "It creates a realistic atmosphere where students may profit from the delivery of a service or product to a small market" (Seymour, 1987, p. 8). The primary advantage in developing a mock company is that it requires students to work together toward a common goal. Henak suggests learning is increased when "students and their ideas become resources and, thus, major elements in the teaching/learning environment" (Kemp & Schwaller, 1988, p. 145). Like most ventures in life, the success of the course depends on the contributions, dedication, and organization of the talents of those in the group.

The inclusion of a classroom enterprise guides the emphasis of the course towards the management and operation of communication industries. A suitable product or type of service must be identified to become the focus of the student enterprise. One possible direction is to create a mock company that will develop a salable product or process (e.g., printed items, typesetting or word processing services, video or cassette tapes, or computer graphics). In this instance, the students can market their in-class developed materials or services for a profit. The second option is to organize an activity that simulates a communication venture but results in a product that is not marketable. For example, the students may prepare for and videotape a half-hour news program, but others are not likely to purchase the completed tape. Another example is when marketable items are actually developed, but local school regulations prohibit the selling of classroom materials or services. Many innovative projects can be developed without a direct exchange of funds. Promotional materials for the school system may help fulfill both the instructional goals and the needs of the school.

A class of this nature is perhaps most appropriate as a synthesis-level class in a communication program. During the course, students should have the opportunity to draw upon their previous experiences, apply insight and creativity to solve divergent problems, and be challenged to work cooperatively with others in the class. While certain content may be prepared prior to the start of the class, the primary purpose of the teacher is to manage and facilitate instruction (rather than direct all course content through lectures, films, etc.).

In summary, a study of mass communication technology and systems is appropriate at the secondary level. Typically, these courses focus on the commercial and technological activities associated with mass communication industries. A common instructional technique is to develop a mock enterprise in the classroom where students learn from the delivery of information, products, or services.

Interdisciplinary Approach

A significant trend in technology-based coursework is to develop educational programs that involve many subjects and disciplines. We are reminded that "the interdisciplinary nature of Technology Education is inherent in its content and strategies for instruction" (ITEA, 1988, p. 11). Zuga observes that "recognizing and integrating the knowledge of other disciplines into a technology education course is teaching with an interdisciplinary approach" (Kemp & Schwaller, 1988, p. 58). This has important implications for the instructor in a communication technology program. Many classes, resources, and facilities in a typical high school are related to the topic of communications technology.

A brief review of any secondary school course list would reveal that many classes feature the application or utilization of communication technology (Figure 5.7). Courses in electronic journalism, typing, data processing, theater, and broadcasting are obvious examples. In addition, instructional resources are usually available in the school's media center and assembly (theater offstage) facility. Numerous opportunities for instructional cooperation and assistance exist in most high schools.

A SAMPLE OF SECONDARY COURSES RELATED TO HUMAN COMMUNICATION

Art
Band
Composition
Data Processing (Typing)
Debate
English
Foreign Languages
Literature
Office Practice
Public Speaking
Journalism
Theater
Typing
Etc.

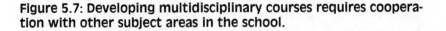

Figure 5.7: Developing multidisciplinary courses requires cooperation with other subject areas in the school.

The complexity of modern communication technology has necessitated new relationships between people and systems. Perhaps Bittner expressed it best when he noted how "it encompasses a multitude of new media and demands the integration of these media in both theory and practice" (1985, p. xv). The potential to exchange ideas and information with others is unparalleled in human history. For instance, one person with a desktop publishing system may replace the combined efforts of editors, artists, drafters, typesetters, graphic layout and composition personnel, and press operators. The product of this type of electronic publishing system might advertise a local bakery sale, promote a political cause, or provide public relations fliers or brochures. At the very least, the individual using the system should understand the application, operation, and implication of this modern technology. Our educational programs must reflect the trend to incorporate multiple technologies at the individual (personal) level.

In summary, secondary coursework in communication systems should complement the mission of the entire technology education program. Of the general program goals identified by Daiber and LaClair, one is to allow students to "participate in multidisciplinary activities in the school curriculum to illustrate the relationship of technology to other subject areas" (Jones & Wright, 1986, p. 97). Attempts to incorporate numerous faculty, students, and disciplines is a worthwhile goal of the high school curriculum.

Nature of an Interdisciplinary Communication Program

Many instructional activities for the study of communication technology and systems would be improved if teachers would identify and draw upon available resources and personnel. Popular classroom and laboratory assignments such as videotaping commercials, developing gaming software, and producing audio recordings are common examples. Other faculty and school staff can contribute significantly to your students' learning. Eventually, it might prove beneficial to team-teach specific courses or units. The following example is designed to illustrate the opportunities of interdisciplinary study.

An interdisciplinary activity in communication classes might be to videotape a short production, such as a 30-second commercial, half-hour news program, or a similar event. The development of a "set" (backdrop, staging, etc.), dressing (furniture, etc.), and props could be completed with the tools and resources in the technology education instructional area. An art teacher and his/her class might be consulted for advice related to colors or shapes of the recording stage. Content for the program could be researched in the school's library with assistance from media personnel. The script might be written in an English class and keyboarded into the computer with the aid of the business or computer instructor and his/her class. A physics teacher might suggest the optimal materials for controlling the noise level in the recording area. Sound and video recording equipment may be demonstrated to students, and the physics classes may assist in researching and testing these aspects with the communication class by the staff from the media center. Rehearsal time for "on-camera" personnel might be supervised by the head of the debate team, the director of the theater department, or a public speaking teacher. Finally, the band or choral director might assist with background music provided by his/her students or help prepare a creative program theme for the production.

Many concepts applied through communication technology and communications systems are based in related school disciplines. Zuga cites the importance of "science" and "mathematics" in understanding photographic processes (Kemp & Schwaller, 1988, p. 68). Broadcasters rely on basic delivery skills learned primarily through language arts courses. Drafters, graphic artists, architects, and technical illustrators receive an extensive background in art and design (Berryman, 1979). Marketing and advertising personnel must understand the psychology of consumers (i.e., their behaviors, attitudes, desires, and buying habits). In theory, practically all educational programs involve some relationship to modern information systems.

The instructor in the communication technology program has many options in developing a broad-based program of study. Perhaps the best strategy is to select activities which, by their nature, require the involvement of other teachers and students in the program or school. A group videotaping project (as the above example) would demand the participation of numerous teachers, staff, and classes. A good working relationship and respect of a colleague's programs are critical to the success of this type of assignment. However, ventures which share the time, talent, and budgets of others are more difficult to schedule.

Another approach is to involve other faculty and students in the technology education area. For instance, students in an advanced communication class may be challenged to (a) develop the advertising media for a manufacturing enterprise course, (b) create audio-visual materials for transportation course content, or (c) prepare and produce a public relations brochure for the entire technology education program. The communication program could also become the prime force behind the production of a school's annual video yearbook.

Finally, constructive partnerships can be developed with area industries and businesses. The educational value of secondary programs can easily be enhanced through the support of local industrial and civic leaders. Field trips, presentations by local "experts," and other support can promote many interdisciplinary ventures. Plus, students may become familiar with exciting career opportunities in allied fields through the vision and enthusiasm displayed by outside professionals.

The Study of Information Processing Techniques

Another approach to structuring a communication program is to base the instructional plan on the conceptual models used to describe modern information processing technologies. Lauda and McCrory note the potential of our discipline when it involves "content and instructional strategies within a laboratory setting which introduces students to technological concepts" (Jones & Wright, 1986, p. 30). A contemporary technology-based program should be founded on generalized concepts that students can utilize throughout a lifetime of change. Kemp and Schwaller (1988) express it this way:

> With the rapid change in technology, it is virtually impossible to remain current with all of the technological developments. So what does the teacher do when the technical scene consistently changes? The answer may be to teach concepts. Concepts contained within the technological systems remain rather constant even though the specific technology changes rapidly. (p. 204)

Bensen (1988) notes the modern practice of identifying and arranging content into categories and hierarchies to facilitate the study of technology. In our case, the focus of the secondary technology education program would conform to activities found in previous courses because they are based on a similar conceptual model. The result is an integrated program that promotes student learning at all levels. Obviously, this has attractive implications as we examine various methods of structuring an upper-level communication program (Figure 5.8).

While the study of communication technology can follow a variety of formats, one of the more common methods is to apply a generalized model to all types of information systems. Hendricks and Sterry (1987) note that most models of the communication process include the information processing tasks of encoding, transmitting, receiving, decoding, storing, and retrieving. Other textbooks used in technology education programs from the junior high through college level also cite these same processes (DuVall, Maughan, & Berger, 1981; Hauenstein & Bachmeyer, 1975; Seymour, Ritz, & Cloughessy, 1987).

INFORMATION PROCESSING TECHNIQUES	
Middle School Activities	ENCODING - Computer programming, graphic layout, etc. TRANSMITTING - On videotape, through wires, etc. RECEIVING - Using stereo receivers, TV antenna, via computer modem, etc. DECODING - Translating Morse Code, watching slides, etc. STORING - Recording images on paper, text on cassette tape, etc. RETRIEVING - Information from card catalogs, etc.
Secondary Activities	ENCODING - Keyboarding, adding sound (special) effects to an audio recording, etc. TRANSMITTING - Using fiber optics signals, through coaxial cables, etc. RECEIVING - With a satellite dish, video systems, etc. DECODING - Translating CNC punch tapes, light-based (digitial) signals, etc. STORING - Experiment with holograms, thermal printers, video disks, etc. RETRIEVING - From computer databases, etc.

Figure 5.8: Examples of communication activities at the middle school and secondary levels. Classroom and laboratories at the high school level should involve more complex technologies.

Organizing the communication technology program coursework around a generalized model has several significant advantages. Students will more readily understand the relationships among various human and technical systems. More importantly, they apply the concepts, information, and skills learned in earlier classes directly to future problems. For example, in working with a fiber optics system during a high school course, students can relate to the concept of digitized signaling due to their introduction to coding systems (Morse Code, ASCII, etc.) in previous classes. In another situation, students may quickly notice that the development of a computerized data base is merely a complex means of storing information. In addition, concepts are reinforced as the students are challenged to apply their ideas and experiences to advanced problems. Finally, Hendricks and Sterry note that "studying concepts not only simplifies the task of understanding systems of today, but also provides a framework for understanding new technologies as they emerge" (1987, p. 54).

Studying Information Processing Techniques

Courses on communication technology and communication systems typically involve a balance of classroom and laboratory assignments. Using this approach, the communication process would become the focus of daily lectures, instructional media, and classroom assignments. Students are given ample opportunities to encode, transmit, receive, decode, store, and retrieve information in various forms during laboratory periods. All procedures, equipment, technologies, etc., used in the course would be linked to one of the six processing techniques. For instance, typesetting and computer programming tasks would be compared to other encoding activities; likewise, magnetic disks and NC punched tape would both be identified as common means of storing information.

The success of this approach is dependent upon the planning of classroom and laboratory activities. Naturally, the instructor should select activities which involve as many of the information processing techniques as possible. The instructor must direct attention to each of the processes involved and compare activities to the elements of the systems model.

This strategy often proves to be quite flexible in structuring advanced topics for students in the secondary program. The nature of most activities can be matched to existing facilities, available time, students' needs, budgets, and other factors. If the resources are not available to demonstrate a laser-based fiber optics system, a related means of transmission can be presented. In a similar manner, the concept of receiving messages or signals can be illustrated with either a TV antenna, modem, satellite dish, or stereo receiver (tuner). The specific instructional plan can be adapted to many laboratory situations and available resources.

In practice, this approach usually evolves into a general yet effective program that features numerous information systems and technologies. The greatest differences between middle school and secondary courses may be in the complexity and depth of the various activities. Both programs require students to practice various information processing techniques. However, activities at the high school level should involve more creative and intellectual challenges. The additional class time permits the instructor to cover each process in greater detail and expect higher levels of achievement as individual activities are completed.

In conclusion, the communication program can easily be structured using a model of basic information-processing technologies. From an instructional viewpoint, it is both helpful and convenient to base both the middle school and secondary program on the same model. Most accepted models include up to six steps or processes that involve encoding, transmitting, receiving, decoding, storage, and retrieval activities. These common information processing tasks can be identified in almost every exchange of information requiring modern technology.

Structures for Implementing Communication Technology Coursework

Various curriculum guides and professional literature suggest program structures for the study of communication. Wright and Sterry (1983, p. 26) propose a simplified "small program, medium program, and large program" model for typical school systems. Boyer (1983) notes the prevalence of courses such as "Basic Communications" in high schools around the nation. More immediate, instructors' manuals are published with most communication textbooks. These publications often specify an instructional plan for the program outlined in the classroom text.

The program models suggested earlier in this chapter provide various means for organizing content for a secondary communication program within the technology education curriculum. However, no single model is appropriate for every school. Each technology education curriculum is dependent upon important elements, including the number of professional staff, facilities, number and length of courses, expected sizes of classes, budget, textbooks, and related factors.

Perhaps the two greatest challenges in developing a "new" communication program within the curriculum are when a single teacher has to develop the entire program, and the difficulties of "phasing in" the new course(s).

This section will offer suggestions for implementing an educational program related to communication systems. The structures presented focus on adapting the nature of the new program to staff, time, and related constraints. In addition, details concerning program growth and the means of updating content are mentioned.

Single Teacher Communication Programs

Few tasks in education are as formidable as developing an entire instructional program from scratch. This is compounded when a single faculty member is faced with the challenge of developing a new program of coursework for communication system instruction. Fortunately, many professional resources, media, and software are available to assist in organizing the program of instruction, classroom facilities, and assignments. In addition, numerous instructional guides and manuals list proven laboratory activities.

Still, it is the responsibility of the classroom teacher to develop an agenda for implementing the communication program. Following the models described earlier in the chapter, the teacher may accomplish implementation of an agenda in one of four ways (Figure 5.9). First, the individual teacher may want to begin with an introductory course that is based on general concepts and systems. This represents one suggested route for a single teacher who decides to phase-in a communication program one course at a time. A second option is to select a particular strength and develop a course that parallels one's interest in either visual (graphic) or audio/audio-visual (electronic) systems. Third, it might be advantageous to begin with an upper-level (mass media, communication enterprise, etc.) course to draw from a student population that has a background in previous industrial arts/education or technology education classes. This advanced course could attract students from related courses in the technology program or from throughout the school. Finally, the instructor may wish to team-teach the initial class with a colleague from a related discipline, thus encouraging an interdisciplinary approach. The benefit in this situation is that the technology education teacher receives valuable assistance from other teachers while improving his/her classroom and laboratory competencies.

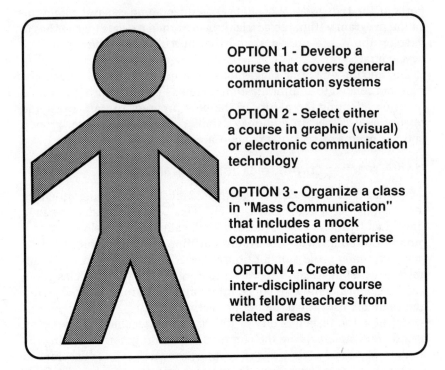

OPTION 1 - Develop a course that covers general communication systems

OPTION 2 - Select either a course in graphic (visual) or electronic communication technology

OPTION 3 - Organize a class in "Mass Communication" that includes a mock communication enterprise

OPTION 4 - Create an inter-disciplinary course with fellow teachers from related areas

Figure 5.9: Suggestions for developing a one-teacher communication program.

The initial course in a communication program may become somewhat of a lesson in "trial and error" for the teacher. After all, it will undoubtedly take time to optimize instructional activities, convert facilities, and develop confidence as an instructor in a new content area. But one should not be dismayed or discouraged. With careful planning and practice, classroom and laboratory activities can be perfected, which motivates both the teacher and the students. Perhaps it is best to remember that we are all "rookies" at various times in our teaching careers, and developing new technology education curriculum is no exception.

After successfully introducing the communication program at the secondary level, plans should be made to expand the course offerings. This may involve implementing a new and different class during each semester, grading period, or academic year. If an electronic communication systems course was initially developed, the next step might be to include a class in graphic technology in the program. In the case where a general course (e.g., Communication Systems I) was offered, an advanced or capstone class might be added. Finally, the instructor might seek outside help in creating an interdisciplinary study of communication technology.

Communication Technology Programs in Larger School Systems

Many medium- to large-sized high schools include technology education departments that feature spacious facilities and several faculty members. These larger programs contain sufficient staff and resources to offer numerous communication courses. However, unique problems often arise in the organization and scheduling of classes. Courses must be designed to minimize an overlap of content, media, and laboratory activities. At the same time, certain faculty must be prepared to teach the complex topics found in upper-level courses. Typically the material included in these advanced courses is highly technical in nature and relies on the knowledge and understanding of emerging technologies. It should also be noted that during the initial offering of advanced courses, many students may be enrolled in classes for which they have not taken suggested prerequisites. These and other problems confront the implementation efforts.

The first basic challenge is to determine which courses to offer at various levels. Most likely, an introductory-level course in communication systems would be offered at the freshman or sophomore level. This course would be designed to review fundamental concepts, plus cover details not addressed in the middle school program. It might be best to develop this course around the general conceptual model proposed earlier in the chapter. The class could be scheduled as a one-semester (half-year) course and consist of primarily "hands-on" activities. Hopefully, this course would prove so popular that multiple sections could be offered.

Next, the curriculum might include either one or more additional courses. In the case of only one more class, appropriate content might be included in either a "Communication Systems II" or a "Mass Communications" course. These courses would supplement the material covered in the introductory classes. In addition, while each course may address independent subject matter, it might be well to make the introductory course a prerequisite for the second-level content.

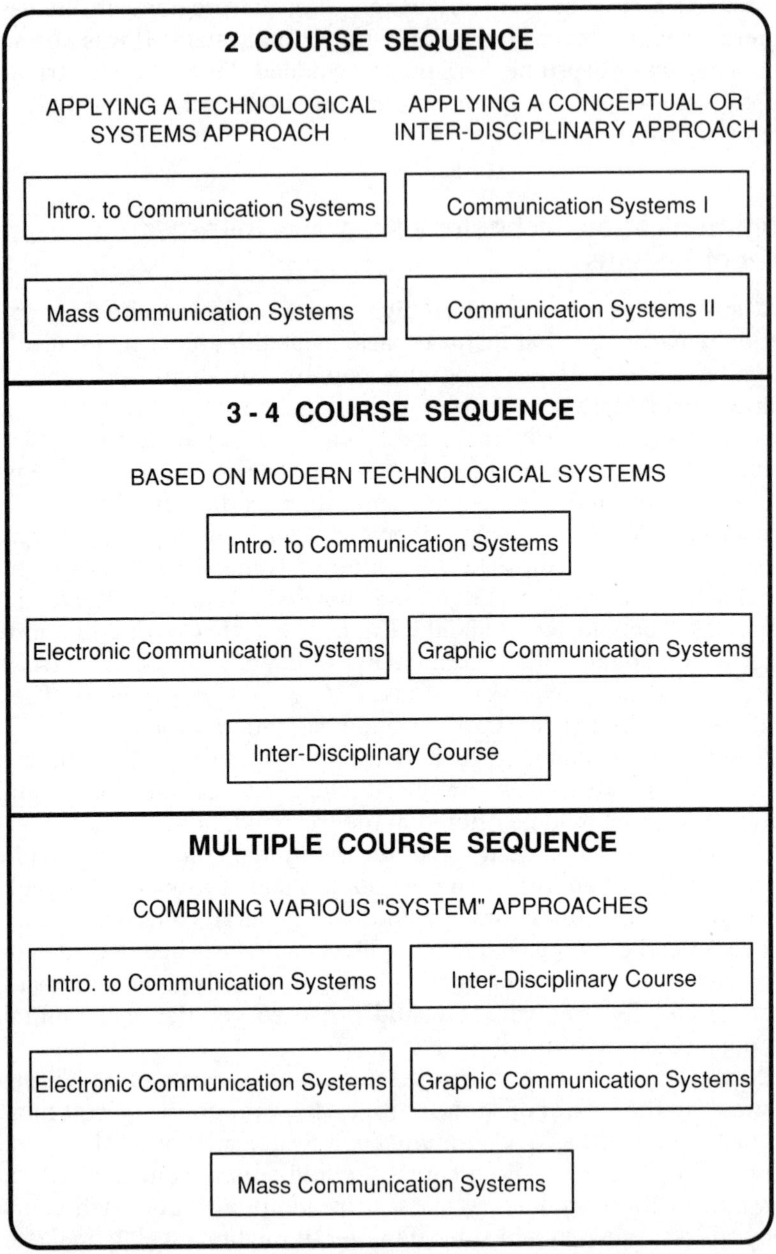

2 COURSE SEQUENCE

APPLYING A TECHNOLOGICAL   APPLYING A CONCEPTUAL OR
SYSTEMS APPROACH   INTER-DISCIPLINARY APPROACH

| Intro. to Communication Systems | Communication Systems I |
| Mass Communication Systems | Communication Systems II |

3 - 4 COURSE SEQUENCE

BASED ON MODERN TECHNOLOGICAL SYSTEMS

Intro. to Communication Systems

Electronic Communication Systems   Graphic Communication Systems

Inter-Disciplinary Course

MULTIPLE COURSE SEQUENCE

COMBINING VARIOUS "SYSTEM" APPROACHES

| Intro. to Communication Systems | Inter-Disciplinary Course |
| Electronic Communication Systems | Graphic Communication Systems |

Mass Communication Systems

Figure 5.10: Various course titles for high school communication technology programs.

If additional courses are to be developed, new titles (and more complex subject matter) are required. The structures shown in Figure 5.10 offer several possibilities for this opportunity. Note the absence of a course based on a "conceptual" approach at the upper levels. Students in advanced courses would still be discovering and applying general concepts at this level. However, by the time an individual has taken three or four courses in an educational program, the focus of the program should go beyond "the basics." Capstone courses ought to address the complex systems used to solve modern technological problems.

Summary

Communication is fundamental to human existence, as are the technical systems used to extend our abilities to exchange ideas and information over varying distances. Without communication technology, modern society would certainly collapse. The ability to live and work successfully in today's information age depends upon an understanding of current devices, systems, and media. It is vital that secondary schools include courses that allow young adults to learn about the application and impact of modern information technology.

Many secondary school disciplines are based on interpersonal and business communication. Yet, few instructional programs promote "technological literacy" related to information systems. This chapter outlined four methods of structuring content in a high school communication technology program. Curricular models and various suggestions for implementing the new programs were discussed. Depending upon the size of the school, a typical technology program might feature three or more separate courses related to communication systems.

The transition of traditional coursework to technology-based programs is not an easy process. However, students expect and deserve instructional programs that prepare them for a technological future. Secondary school teachers must accept the challenge of up-dating their curriculum to match emerging trends in technology.

References

Adamson, T. A. (1988). *Electronic communications: Systems and circuits.* Albany, NY: Delmar Publishers.

Baldwin, T. F. & McVoy, D. S. (1983). *Cable communication.* Englewood Cliffs, NJ: Prentice-Hall Inc.

Bensen, M. J. (1988). The transition from industrial arts to technology education. In Brandt, R. S. (Eds.), *Content of the curriculum.* pp. 167-180. Alexandria, VA: Association of Supervision and Curriculum Development.

Berryman, G. (1979). *Notes on graphic design and visual communication.* Los Altos, CA: William Kauffman, Inc.

Bittner, J. R. (1985). *Broadcasting and telecommunication* (2nd ed.). Englewood Cliffs, NJ: Prentice-Hall, Inc.

Book, A. C., Cary, N. D., & Tannenbaum, S. I. (1984). *The radio & television commercial.* (2nd ed.). Lincolnwood, IL: National Textbook Company.

Boyer, E. L. (1983). *High school: A report on secondary education in America.* New York: Harper & Row.

Burke, T. J. M. & Lehman, M. (Eds.). (1981). *Communication technologies and information flow.* New York: Pergamon Press.

Burrows, T. & Wood, D. (1982). *Television production* (2nd ed.). Dubuque, IA: William C. Brown, Inc.

Cannon, D. L. & Luecke, G. (1984). *Understanding communications systems.* Dallas, TX: Texas Instruments.

Colelli, L. A. (1989). *Technology education: A primer.* Reston, VA: International Technology Education Association.

Churchman, C. W. (1979). *The systems approach* (rev. ed.). New York: Dell Publishing.

Craig, J. (1974). *Production for the graphic designer.* New York: Watson-Guptill Publications.

Dordick, H. S. (1986). *Understanding modern telecommunications.* New York: McGraw-Hill Book Company.

DuVall, J. B., Maughan, G. R., Jr., & Berger, E. G. (1981). *Getting the message: The technology of communication.* Worcester, MA: Davis Publications.

Fuller, B. J., Kanaba, S., & Brisch-Kanaba, J. (1982). *Single-camera video production.* Englewood Cliffs, NJ: Prentice-Hall, Inc.

Goodlad, J. I. (1984). *A place called school.* New York: McGraw-Hill Book Company.

Gross, L. S. (1983). *Telecommunications: An introduction to radio, television, and the developing media.* Dubuque, IA: William C. Brown, Inc.

Hanks, K., Belliston, L., & Edwards, D. (1978). *Design yourself!* Los Altos, CA: William Kaufman, Inc.

Hauenstein, A. D., & Bachmeyer, S. A. (1975). *The world of communications.* Peoria, IL: Glencoe Publishing.

Head, S. W. & Sterling, C. H. (1987). *Broadcasting in America* (5th ed.). Boston, MA: Houghton Mifflin Company.

Hendricks, R. W. & Sterry, L. F. (1987). *Communication technology.* Menomonie, WI: T & E Publications.

Inose, H. & Pierce, J. R. (1984). *Information technology and civilization.* New York: W. H. Freeman and Company.

International Technology Education Association. (1988). *Technology: A national imperative.* Reston, VA: Author.

International Technology Education Association. (1985). *Technology education: A perspective on implementation.* Reston, VA: Author.

Jones, R. E. & Robb, J. L. (1986). *Discovering technology: Communication.* Orlando, FL: Harcourt Brace Jovanovich.

Jones, R. E. & Wright, J. R. (Eds.). (1986). *Implementing Technology Education*, 35th Yearbook, American Council on Industrial Arts Teacher Education.

Kahaner, L. (1986). *On the air.* New York: Warner Books.

Kemp, W. H. & Schwaller, A. E. (Eds.) (1988). *Instructional strategies for technology education*, 37th Yearbook, Council on Technology Teacher Education.

Marchand, D. A. & Horton, F. W., Jr. (1986). *Infotrends: Profiting from your information resources.* New York: John Wiley & Sons.

Marsh, K. (1982). *The way the new technology works.* New York: Fireside Books (Simon & Schuster).

Pember, D. R. (1987). *Mass media in America* (5th ed.). Chicago, IL: Science Research Associates.

Radlow, J. (1986). *Computers and the information society.* New York: McGraw-Hill Book Company.

Rogers, E. M. (1986). *Communication technology: The new media in society.* New York: Free Press.

Runyon, K. E. (1979). *Advertising and the practice of marketing.* Columbus, OH: Charles E. Merrill Publishing (Bell & Howell).

Schrank, J. (1986). *Understanding mass media* (3rd ed.). Lincolnwood, IL: National Textbook Company.

Seymour, R. D., Ritz, J. M., & Cloughessy, F. A. (1987). *Exploring communication.* South Holland, IL: The Goodheart-Wilcox Co., Inc.

Seymour, R. D. (1987). *Instructor's guide for exploring communications.* South Holland, IL: The Goodheart-Wilcox Co., Inc.

Weinstein, B. (1984). *Breaking into communications.* New York: Arco Publishing, Inc.

Wright, R. T. & Sterry, L. (1983). *Industry and technology education: A guide for curriculum designers, implementors, and teachers.* San Marcos, TX: Technical Foundation of America.

Wurman, R. S. (1989). *Information anxiety.* New York: Doubleday.

Chapter 6

RATIONALE AND CONCEPTUAL MODELS FOR COMMUNICATION TECHNOLOGY IN TECHNOLOGY TEACHER EDUCATION

Leonard F. Sterry
Professor
and
Robert Hendricks
Associate Professor
Graphic Communications Department
University of Wisconsin-Stout
Menomonie, Wisconsin

Communication in Technology Teacher Education

Very few people will dispute the fact that technology is advancing at a pace that has never before been experienced by humankind. Future projections show no indication that this rate of change will slow or decrease. In fact, most indications suggest that the rate of technological growth will increase significantly.

At one time those of us in the United States thought of ourselves as leaders in technological development. This notion is no longer true, if in fact it was ever the case. Technology is advancing at an accelerated pace throughout the world. It has become a global phenomenon as never before. As a result, the world has become a community, one that is highly interdependent.

Change has occurred in many aspects of human endeavor; however, few areas have changed more than that of communication. Our ability to move information is awesome. We move it around our homes, the workplace, and around the world at rates that are nearly instantaneous.

We interact with technology on an everyday basis. We are affected by it whether we realize it or not. It affects the food we eat, the products we consume, the shelter we live in, the security we enjoy, our medical services, our transportation systems, and the way in which we communicate. We possess an enormous capability in our technology, yet how many of us as citizens in a democratic society truly understand this potential? Some suggest we know very little about technology, even though we live with it and make decisions about it everyday -- for good and for bad. It, therefore, seems essential that as citizens in a global society, we study technology as an integral part of our education at all levels.

Many school districts across the nation are responding by initiating programs of technology education. These programs are designed to help students gain an understanding of technology and the impacts that it is having on all of us. A part of understanding technology includes understanding communication.

As school districts implement programs of technology education, they need new teachers who are trained in the concepts of technology education. In addition, they need to have existing teachers retrained, or at least updated, to teach about technology. This requires the universities that prepare teachers to update their programs if they are going to be able to respond to this evolving and growing need in teacher training and retraining. And that, in itself, is a challenge with several dimensions. This chapter deals with a variety of those factors.

Curriculum Models and Their Importance

During recent years, there has been a considerable amount of curriculum work in the area of technology education. This work has been largely directed at designing programs that will help students gain an understanding of technology and its impacts. Later in this chapter some of the more significant developments in the evolutionary process are discussed.

Largely as a result of these changes, teacher education has had to change. In some instances, universities were the initiators of the change and were on the leading edge. Other times, unfortunately, they were reluctant followers of change. In any event, whether at the secondary or university level, most curriculum efforts result in models -- models of technology education and models of the components of technology education. One of those components, in most contemporary curriculum designs, is the study of communication. And that, at the university level, is the focus of this chapter.

Models are important in that they help to define and organize an idea. They usually end up being a product; however, the real value of a model may be in the purpose it serves as a process of thinking. Most models are based on some rationale, purpose, or mission. For example, technology education is based on the premise that technology is a significant force in modern society, that it is worthy of study in our schools, and that technology education is the subject best suited to deliver this instruction to students. Yet, when this intent is interpreted, it results in many different models.

The same is true with communication technology. Many of us will agree that it is an area worthy of study. We believe it should be taught at both the secondary and university levels of education. However, the interpretation of that intent varies; and, as a result, so do the models.

Some, for example, choose to gather content from other subjects and assign new titles to the courses or experiences. Others choose to cluster content from different technologies, industries, or occupations. Still others believe there is a unique body of content that is derived from an analysis of the technology. All are models; all are interpretations; all, to some degree or another, can be reasoned to be correct. Thus, models are powerful in the thinking process.

The Study of Developmental Efforts

As technology teachers are prepared to teach about communication technology, it is essential that they understand the developmental and philosophical basis for the study of communication systems within the technology education curriculum. The evolution of content that has occurred is well documented in the professional literature (see also Chapter 3). Over the course of the past twenty years, many models have been developed in an attempt to define the content base for industrial arts, and now technology education. Many of those models included some kind of a subset or provision for communication, either as a concept in the broader sense of industry, or as a echnology worthy of study in itself.

William Warner was among the first to work with curriculum in the area of technology, and specifically, communication. Dr. Warner's work included a "Communications Division" in *A Curriculum to Reflect Technology*. His proposal introduced a communications division that was conceptually organized. An outline of the section follows:

A Curriculum To Reflect Technology
The Communications Division

Telegraphy	Composition and Duplication
Telephone	Graphic Arts
Sound Recording	Drawing, Sketching
Drafting, Blueprinting	Letterpress
Transmission and Reception	Mechanical-Electrical
Radio	Photography
Teletype	Intagliography
Planography	Television
Duplicating	Facsimile
Sound Recording	Multi-Channel Methods
Radar	Visual, Sound and Codes
Historical	Signal Flags
Lights	Sound Devices

American Industry was one of twenty or more projects during the late 1960's and early 1970's that attempted to define the content base for industrial arts. The project viewed communication as one of thirteen concepts that are a part of all industries. And, just like the other concepts, communication was further defined by a set of subconcepts. The American Industry Project treated communication as a concept or major idea. It did not attempt to identify structure for communication technology or the communication industry. Following is a conceptual breakout for the concept of communication as viewed by the project.

American Industry Communications Concepts

Source	Vehicle
System	Receiver
Feedback	Interference

In a recent dissertation, Jerry Richter (1980) created and validated a test for technological literacy in the area of communication. This work is of interest not only because of the test, but also because of how Richter identified the body of knowledge for communication from which he constructed test items. Richter chose not to use content for communication that was identified by the industrial arts profession, perhaps acknowledging the lack of such a content model. Instead, he used a portion of Melvin Kranzberg's *Technology in Western Civilization.*

At least two additional projects have had a significant impact on industrial arts/technology education in the secondary schools and thus, technology teacher education. Those two projects are the Jackson's Mill Curriculum Theory and the Curriculum Implementation Project. Because they are relatively new and because they have had possibly the greatest impact of all recent projects in our field, these two projects will be treated in a little more detail and emphasis than earlier works. This might begin to sound a bit like a repeat of secondary school curriculum, but these two projects have the potential of having a significant impact on teacher education and, to some degree, they already have.

Jackson's Mill Curriculum Theory

Between the time when selected trades served as content organizers and about 1980, industrial arts was in a state of confusion. Many professionals knew that curriculum based on woodworking, metalworking, drafting, and the like, was no longer appropriate. This dissatisfaction caused the innovative era of the 1960's and '70's to evolve. The research of that time suggested that the content base for industrial arts should be derived from an analysis of industry, and that this was different than the trades.

As a result, the profession was divided between those advocating innovation, and those arguing that change was not needed. To add to the confusion, the innovators themselves could not agree on a unified direction. It was not until about 1980 that some consensus was reached about the direction of industrial arts. That consensus was an outcome of the Jackson's Mill Project. It is probably the most notable curriculum effort in recent years.

This curriculum effort identified what has become the most widely accepted content organization for industrial arts since woodworking, metalworking, and drafting. It has helped to establish technology as the agreed upon content base for what is now technology education.

The Jackson's Mill Curriculum Theory identified domains of knowledge and human adaptive systems as the basis for curriculum development (see Figure 6.1). The domains of knowledge include the sciences, the humanities, the technologies, and formal knowledge. These domains provide an organization for human knowledge. They provide the knowledge base that enables us to manage our environment. And, it is noteworthy that one of the domains is the technologies. This suggests that there is a body of knowledge that is

96

technological. It will be a major challenge to the profession to agree upon a definition and body of content that is representative of technology.

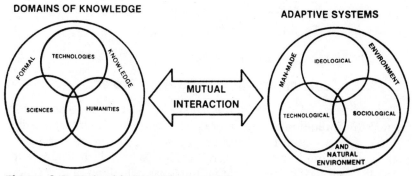

Figure 6.1: Mutual interaction model.

The Jackson's Mill effort also identified human adaptive systems. These are systems that, as a society, we created to serve our needs. The systems are ideological, sociological, and technological. Ideological systems are concerned with the values and beliefs of society. Sociological systems are patterns of societal endeavor, characterized by social organization and regulation. Technological systems pertain to our means of manipulating the physical world to meet our basic needs and wants.

The technological systems were defined by the project to include the subsystems of communication, construction, manufacturing, and transportation. They were derived on the notion that we have always adapted our environment to suit our needs and desires via these methods. As we developed a need to exchange ideas and information, and to move ourselves and things from one location to another, we created systems of communication and transportation. And as we developed a need to produce products for our consumption and comfort, and to shelter ourselves and our possessions, we also created systems for manufacturing and construction. We created systems of technology to extend our potential as human beings, and thus, satisfy some of our material needs. Each subsystem was further defined by a set of unique concepts. Communication was defined by the authors of the project as, "a technical adaptive system designed by people to efficiently utilize resources to transfer information to extend human potential." The work went on to identify the following concepts of communication.

Communication Concepts

Encoding	Storing
Transmitting	Retrieving
Receiving	Decoding
Feedback	

Curriculum Implementation Project

The Jackson's Mill Curriculum Theory was just that, a theory. It needed interpretation and development. That need for interpretation led to the Curriculum Implementation Project. The primary purpose of the Curriculum Implementation Project was to add sufficient detail to the Jackson's Mill Theory so that the ideas contained in that report could be used by school districts, departments of education, and universities for curriculum improvement. As a result, the project accepted the Jackson's Mill work, including the subsystem communication. The project further accepted the conceptual framework that was developed for each subsystem.

The Curriculum Implementation Project (CIP) developed a set of some twenty courses; each course was complete with title, description, objectives, content, suggested activities, and method of student evaluation. The courses were further organized into models appropriate for schools with small, medium, and large programs. With the exception of communication systems, coursework was based on the concepts of the subsystems.

In the case of communication systems, the concepts identified by Jackson's Mill included encoding, transmitting, receiving, decoding, storing, and retrieving. Yet, when the coursework was developed, titles such as media communications were used. There was little use of the concepts in the courses. Those who worked on CIP had little time and little previous work to draw upon. As a result, courses were largely based on a collection of content from existing courses rather than on concepts unique to communication. For the most part, the CIP work, along with Jackson's Mill, contributed very positively to the evolution of technology education.

Factors to Consider
in Selecting an Appropriate Model

Although many models exist, it is important to develop or accept a model of a discipline or subject as a first step in developing courses and course sequences. In developing and accepting a model, it is important to select one that is a legitimate organizer of the field of study. The model must be a holistic view of the field, as well as one that serves to integrate various facets of the field. It must be dynamic, and thus able to expand and change as the field expands and changes. This ability to integrate new knowledge into an existing framework is the key factor in selecting a model.

After a model is selected, courses and activities can be developed. We often rush to start developing activities rather than first creating an accurate picture of the discipline we want students to understand.

Using Our Heritage

Our heritage of industrial arts, and now technology education, will be a factor in the type of model selected or created. Although it will always be a factor, it cannot be the dominant force. For example, we often see models for communication that suggest a little drafting, graphic arts, photography, and electronics all forced together. That's our heritage showing. To be truly objective in selecting a model, we must look to redefine the field of study, and not merely put pieces of our curricular past together to suggest we now have a holistic program for the study of communication.

The Textbook Approach

Another way of selecting a model is to simply adopt a textbook. By following this method, we are assuming the publisher or the authors have given great thought to the model from which they generated the text for the book. This assumption may or may not be true. More often than not, the authors will use their own line of reasoning for the model. It might be well researched, but most likely it will be a collection of the familiar literature based in part on their curricular past.

However, regardless of what the author might think, the publisher must adopt a model that will sell. Or, in other words, what is the field ready to buy? Publishers will often submit a manuscript to readers to help determine the readiness of the field. As a result, models and curriculum based on textbooks may be conservative and focused on the past rather than on the future. The last few comments are not intended to be a criticism of publishers, they are in business for profit. Some are progressive and future oriented. They want to reach forward to the limits of what the field is ready to accept, but at the same time, they have to be realistic if they want to sell books. The comments are mostly a criticism of our field and how slowly it responds to change -- both at the secondary school level and in teacher education. In fact, publishers deserve a great deal of credit for their objectivity, leadership, support, and commitment to the field of technology education.

Clustering

Clustering has been another way to derive curricular models. This has been a process of both drawing on our heritage and looking for a few new bits of content that might conveniently fit under a new title. Some of the clustering thinking comes from vocational education. As vocational education moved from specific job preparation, clustering jobs or occupations became popular and curriculum was often based on those clusters.

Clustering has been a common means by which communication has been organized. We see it in local school curriculum, state curriculum guides, university coursework, and textbooks. Clustering in communication is usually a collection of some graphic arts, photography, drafting, and electronics and putting this content under a new title. By clustering, the risk that sometimes comes with a total commitment is avoided. In this way, we reached out a bit, but not so far as to get into unfamiliar territory. This technique enabled us to get at some communication related content that we all could understand. So in essence, we had both security and familiarity. In all fairness, however, it should be pointed out that clustering provided a palatable transition from a trade-oriented industrial arts to a concept-based technology education.

At one time clustering was justifiable, but not any longer. Thanks to the efforts of those involved with the Jackson's Mill Project and the work that has followed, we are at a point in our development where we can philosophically deal with different kinds of thinking. Clustering avoids addressing the true intent and emphasis of a technology-based curriculum such as applied in technology education. Our recommendation on clustering: Start that way if you must, but move to a conceptual organization as quickly as possible. Some of the activities developed for clusters will be useful in developing a concept-based program in communication.

Conceptual Organization

A concept is an idea or thought that creates a mental image. There are big concepts and there are little concepts, just as there are big and little ideas. Concepts can be isolated thoughts; however, they usually come from some very large idea or phenomenon. For example, in technology education we are trying to deal with the phenomenon of technology. That's the big idea, and this big idea is made up of other smaller ideas or concepts. Although we have tried to determine what those small ideas might be, we have not been able to establish an adequate hierarchy or taxonomy for technology. Yet, there must be a set of smaller ideas that would help to describe the complex concept of technology.

Conceptual taxonomies provide content stability in an age that is frequently characterized as one of rapid change. More than just stability, however, studying concepts provides students with experiences that teach the intellectual process of identifying organized relationships among the many complex facets of our world. We all need to be able to look at different situations and sort these individual experiences into categories that have common characteristics. Furthermore, once a person has a fundamental understanding of a set of concepts that make up a given discipline, he or she then has the tools to easily integrate new knowledge into a sphere of understanding.

A concept also represents a class of ideas. Each class must have an identifiable set of characteristics. These characteristics help to make it possible to examine an idea and then place it into a logical class. Concepts are best formed by exploration (heuristics) rather than by step-by-step procedural methods (algorithmics). And, there are rules by which concepts are formulated.

Rules of Formulating Concepts:
1. A field of study or "whole" must be accurately defined before subconcepts are identified.
2. Concepts must be mutually exclusive.
3. Concepts must be totally inclusive.
4. Concepts must be operationally adequate.
5. Concepts must have characteristics or identifiable attributes that enable a person to distinguish between exemplars and nonexemplars.
6. Concepts must have recognizable names that are understandable by others.
7. Concepts must show clusters of interrelatedness when examined through attributes and exemplars.
8. Subordinate or lower order concept classifications must be established that are totally incumbent within the higher order concepts.
9. Concept taxonomies must be tested by trying to logically classify a variety of examples that are clearly a part of the discipline.

Taxonomies are essentially a hierarchy of concepts. A taxonomy is the sorting of ideas into categories or groupings by level of magnitude or significance. So in a curriculum sense, when we talk about a conceptual model, we are usually talking about a series of concepts that are ordered as a taxonomy or hierarchy. And in this lies the power of a conceptual model -- a sorted set of key thoughts about a major phenomenon.

How do we know when we are correct about the conceptual model? Verifying and validating the accuracy of knowledge is a process of growing importance. For example, the taxonomy that will be presented for communication technology later in this chapter is the product of a carefully planned series of events that verified the breadth and depth of the taxonomy. Validating a taxonomy usually makes use of persons who possess expertise in given fields of study. Different methods have been used to gather information from these experts, and thus make use of their collective expertise in creating and validating a taxonomy. The fundamental ingredient in any validation is to first assemble the right group of people with the right expertise, and then to ask them the right questions. After receiving responses to the questions, it is important to modify the taxonomy accordingly. Commonly used strategies for interrogating experts includes the Delphi technique, face-to-face expert panel discussions, and industry analyses or questionnaires. A well developed taxonomy of technical concepts should clearly define the field of study as it is found today. The taxonomy should also provide a structure for understanding new technical developments which are about to occur. Many new technologies are not totally new but rather adoptions or adaptations of an existing technology.

A taxonomy of concepts should provide a framework for integrating new technological developments. A simple example might help to make this point more clear. If we were to ask a group of students how a hologram works, many would probably have some difficulty explaining the process. However, if we asked a group of students how black and white photography works, we would probably get some discussion about exposing film, controlling light, developing film, and the like. The argument for a conceptual understanding of this specific communication technology is that holography is not a radically new technology, but rather an application of encoding and storing concepts that have been used in black and white photography for a long time.

It is usually easier to understand an unfamiliar technology if a person can relate the development to a concept that is familiar. This is especially true in communication, where rapid technological change is a given. It would be extremely difficult for many of us to keep abreast of all that is happening in communication. However, the task is easier if we can relate new developments to a set of familiar concepts.

Communication technology is an area where traditional boundaries are evaporating. The printing and publishing field, for example, is now heavily computerized and makes extensive use of telecommunications. The publishing of the national newspaper, *USA Today*, is a good example of this blurring of traditional content boundaries.

New approaches need to be developed for the study of communication technology. An approach is needed that integrates rather than segregates related technologies. We can no longer teach graphic arts, electronics, and drafting as separate subjects if we expect students to see, much less understand, the dynamic interrelationships that exist within these fields. If we want students to see relationships between various related technologies in the field of communication, then we have to teach relationships. We cannot continue to teach different technologies in isolation and expect students to somehow pull these segments of instruction together into a holistic understanding of communication systems.

A taxonomy is just that, a taxonomy. It is not a curriculum guide; it is not a course outline; it does not contain all of the content that one might determine appropriate for the study of communication. A taxonomy is the detailing of the technical processes of communication and, as such, should be a tool used in the instructional development process.

Other curriculum elements must also be addressed in designing instruction. For example, no course or program would be complete without looking at regulations, policy issues, or social/cultural implications of the technology. While the taxonomy defines technical concepts, other issues must be addressed if a meaningful instructional program is to be developed. It would be undesirable and inappropriate to produce students who understood the technical side of a technological system without also understanding the human dimension.

The Technology Teacher Education Situation

The transition to technology education was prompted by rapid developments in technology, international competition in the market place, a changing society, and a reassessment of personal beliefs. These and other factors have collectively caused a need for a different kind of education for the young people of the United States and the world in general.

As this change occurred, teachers were asked to teach content that was different from what they taught as a part of the industrial arts curriculum. They were asked to teach about technology. Yet, this concept was new, unfamiliar, and threatening to many. In addition, there was a lot of controversy about first, teaching technology, and second, what should be taught in the name of technology and who should teach it.

As was already discussed in Chapter 3, the Jackson's Mill project clearly identified communication as one of the human adaptive systems worthy of study as a part of technology education. It is mentioned again here only to emphasize the point that if communication is identified as appropriate content for elementary and secondary education, then it seems only logical that it become a part of teacher education and especially technology teacher education.

Historically, teacher education has been slow to adopt change. Teacher educators have made great speeches, developed good models, and prompted others to change, but they, themselves, have been reluctant to change. This has been true in both the technology that is taught and the philosophy professed. Part of the problem has been that teacher education was not willing to take the risk of a commitment and was unsure of what changes were appropriate in a technological sense. Another factor is that some teacher educators were as tied to tradition as anyone. Many were prepared during an era of trade training and, as a result, were simply not prepared to teach about technology either, at least not without a lot of commitment and additional work.

There were several other factors that influenced the adoption of technology education and communication technology, some legitimate and others not. Questions were sometimes asked about the extent to which teacher education should lead or follow. That is, how far ahead should teacher education get beyond what is typically happening in schools? Or, should teacher educators wait to see what local schools and state departments of education are advocating before making adjustments in teacher education?

The answer to these questions always seemed apparent, but it varied by individuals and institutions. It seems good judgment is the best answer. First, teacher educators must take a leadership posture in technology teacher education. Questioning this position is totally inappropriate. Secondly, colleges and universities must find that fine line of reaching out with change to the very limits of what can be accepted by the state or region that is being served, while keeping in mind the limits of what the university staff can accept. There is a danger of being too cautious. If an error is to be made, it should be to the side of being overly progressive rather than too conservative.

New teachers can learn conventional techniques if put in a situation where that is required. There is a lot of material available to help, and with the proper philosophical mindset, the new teacher will be able to adjust. However, if we err to the conservative side, it will be more difficult for a new teacher to adjust, both technically and philosophically. They won't have the right orientation, teaching skills, desire, or determination. As a result, they will be likely to drift back to tradition when the going gets tough or they are put in a conventional situation, perhaps with a peer group that refuses to change.

Another aspect of the argument is that classroom teachers won't buy a new organization of content. We simply need to work through the difficulties together. It is important to have teachers who accept and promote the concept of a new organization for all content and this includes communication. Not only do we need examples and model programs, we need progressive cooperating schools who will take student teachers.

The Curriculum Implementation Project that followed the Jackson's Mill effort used organizers such as graphic communication and electronic communication. But that was inconsistent with the intent of Jackson's Mill. In the Implementation Guide, the courses under the other organizers tended to be consistent with the systems from which they came. Manufacturing, for example, was not organized on the basis of wood, metal, and plastic; but more thought had already gone into the area of manufacturing during the innovative years of the 1960's. This clearly suggests that if communication is a viable area of study, the major concepts identified in the Jackson's Mill Theory and more appropriate organizers must emerge. That will happen now that more information is available on how to organize communication for study and because the profession is more ready to make a total commitment to technology education.

The Curriculum Process

The subconcepts of communication have been identified as encoding, transmitting, receiving, storing, retrieving, decoding and feedback. While these are appropriate concepts, neither Jackson's Mill or the Curriculum Implementation Project defined the concepts or identified the subconcepts for use in curriculum development. In a carefully designed study, Bob Hendricks validated these concepts with a panel of experts. He assembled a panel of experts in communication technology and, using a Delphi technique, asked the panel to validate the Jackson's Mill communication concepts and to help identify additional subconcepts. It is important to note that the panel was asked about communication technology, not clusters, not graphic arts or photography, not the status of industrial arts, but communication technology.

The study resulted in a conceptual taxonomy that is appropriate for the study of communication technology at any level of instruction, including technology teacher education. This model includes only second order concepts. The full taxonomy provides three levels of specificity.

Concepts of Communication Technology

Encoding - The technical processes which recode or modify information into a desired format or pattern for a specific method of transmission or storage.
  Subconcepts
    Designing
    Converting acoustical energy
    Converting light energy
    Converting mechanical energy
    Converting heat energy
Transmitting - The technical processes of conveying information from one location to another.
  Subconcepts
    Modulating
    Amplifying
    Multiplexing
    Duplexing
    Frequency selecting
    Propagating
    Signal conditioning
    Switching
Receiving - The technical processes of recognizing and accepting information that has been transmitted.
  Subconcepts
    Collecting
    Connecting
    Amplifying
    Demodulating
    Demultiplexing
Storing - The technical processes of recording and filing information for use at a later time.
  Subconcepts
    Separating
    Coating
    Conditioning
    Forming

Retrieving - The technical processes of recalling information from a stored condition.
Subconcepts
Abstracting
Indexing
Accessing
Controlling
Decoding - The technical processes of converting recorded or modified information into an acceptable format for use.
Subconcepts
Converting electrical energy
Projecting
Reflecting

Deriving Curriculum from a Taxonomy

Usually a program will require more than one course in communication technology or systems. But if only one course is needed for the start of a technology teacher education program, or if several are being developed for a sequence, the procedure is about the same. In either case, a base or introductory course should be developed. And regardless of the students who are being served, the technical portion of the course will remain the same.

A first course in communication must cover all of the major concepts of the taxonomy. In this instance, those concepts are encoding, transmitting, receiving, storing, retrieving, and decoding. Covering all six concepts will provide students with a broadly based conceptual understanding of communication. This method of deriving content will only provide the technical content of the course. Other factors should also be considered. Course objectives based on issues, policy, regulation, ethics, history, and futures will help to provide additional direction for the selection of supporting content.

When second-level courses are developed, there are two directions from which to select. One direction is that of a spiral, whereby each concept is treated in additional depth by going deeper into the taxonomy so that second and third order concepts can be addressed. A second course in a spiral fashion can serve either as a single upper-level experience or it can serve along with a combination of other courses in an upper-level sequence. Figure 6.2, on the next page, is presented to clarify this idea.

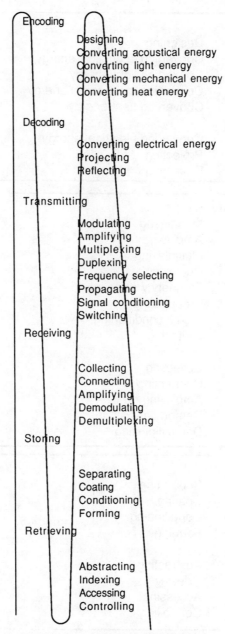

Encoding

Designing
Converting acoustical energy
Converting light energy
Converting mechanical energy
Converting heat energy

Decoding

Converting electrical energy
Projecting
Reflecting

Transmitting

Modulating
Amplifying
Multiplexing
Duplexing
Frequency selecting
Propagating
Signal conditioning
Switching

Receiving

Collecting
Connecting
Amplifying
Demodulating
Demultiplexing

Storing

Separating
Coating
Conditioning
Forming

Retrieving

Abstracting
Indexing
Accessing
Controlling

Figure 6.2: Spiral approach through the concepts.

Encoding
> Designing
> Converting acoustical energy
> Converting light energy
> Converting mechanical energy
> Converting heat energy

Decoding
> Converting electrical energy
> Projecting
> Reflecting

Transmitting
> Modulating
> Amplifying
> Multiplexing
> Duplexing
> Frequency selecting
> Propagating
> Signal conditioning
> Switching

Receiving
> Collecting
> Connecting
> Amplifying
> Demodulating
> Demulitiplexing

Storing
> Separating
> Coating
> Conditioning
> Forming

Retrieving
> Abstracting
> indexing
> Accessing
> Controlling

Figure 6.3: Grouping concepts for courses.

Figure 6.3 shows how upper-level courses can be generated by in-depth treatment with only several concepts in a given course. When using this technique, only compatible concepts should be combined into a course. Developing courses in this way can be appropriate as a follow-up to either the first course or a second course in a sequence if the spiral idea is used.

Relationships to Existing Technology Courses

Many technology teacher education programs, because of other degree options within the department, may not have coursework in communication, yet they probably have courses in areas such as graphic arts, photography, drafting, and electronics. If a program elects to develop coursework in communication, does that mean they must throw away all that they were doing in conventional courses? The answer is, "no!" What they need to do is put the existing content into perspective, a perspective of communication concepts. So why change if we are going to use the same old content? The answer goes back to the rationale for conceptual development explained earlier in the chapter. If we help students understand major concepts, they take with them from the learning experience a content for change, future learning, and application.

If a student, on the other hand, studies graphic arts, he or she will have an understanding of that content, but probably not of communication content simply because that content was never covered. Therefore, the student will never see the relationship of graphic arts processes to the broad area of communication. However, if students study communication, they will understand graphic arts processes and how these processes fit into the broad spectrum of communication and the relationship of those processes to other communication concepts.

How does a course such as graphic arts, for example, fit into this scheme? Very nicely. A typical course in graphic arts usually includes some design work, electronic composition, photographic processes, and putting ink onto a substrate. Designing is an encoding process, and photography is a storing concept. Putting ink on a substrate is also a storing concept. When this is done in mass, however, the process is actually a manufacturing concept. So does it fit? Yes it fits, but it depends to a large extent on what the curriculum designer really wants to accomplish in a program of technology teacher education.

A Relationship to
General Education and Other Majors

Recent professional discussions have included teaching technology as a part of a comprehensive program of general education at the college or university level. This is based on the rationale that one can hardly be liberally educated without some understanding of technology and its impacts on the way we live and work. This is by no means a new concept to many. It is, however, a difficult concept to put in place on many campuses.

A study of technology can be approached in different ways. One logical approach is to design general courses that deal with the subject. Such an approach might include such courses as Understanding Technology, Futures of Technology, History of Technology, and Impacts of Technology. These courses could be followed by more specific coursework in an area such as Communication Technology. A study of communication technology could be rationalized on the premise that communication is having such a significant impact on every aspect of society.

Regardless of how it is justified, if coursework is developed for general education purposes, the developmental process is the same as that described for technology teacher education. In fact, the same process will be suggested in the discussion of the relationship of communication to other university programs and majors. Communication technology is communication technology. The reasons for learning it and the application may vary, but the technology remains the same. As a result, such coursework is easily justified and is appropriate to many university level students, in addition to the technology education majors. If a department is looking for enrollments, this is a lucrative area to consider. It is exciting, provocative, and glamorous to many nontechnical students.

The study of technology and specifically communication systems can also be an important component in other majors. It can be reasoned that whatever career a student might pursue, communication will be an important part of that career area. And, some students will choose careers specifically in some facet of communication. Students in management and business programs will one day manage the technology. Students in applied technology and engineering will design components and systems of communication. All, of course, will be users of the technology.

As coursework is developed, it is appropriate to keep all users in mind. Often, with just a little compromise, one course will fulfill the needs of several majors. This is especially important where the number of students and available resources will not warrant more than one course in a similar area of instruction. There may be an advantage in having students from different majors in the same class. From both an administrative and instructional point of view, a strong case can be made for not developing discrete courses, at least at the introductory level, for students of different majors.

Philosophically, some might argue that mixing majors is inappropriate. This could cause an inconvenience for those who teach instructional methods as a part of a technical sequence of courses. However, this too can be accommodated by offering a slightly different set of activities for students of different majors for purposes of accomplishing different objectives.

A Look Ahead

This chapter was dedicated to a curriculum perspective of communication in technology teacher education. However, for many of us, this is different from what we were taught when we were in school. Therefore, if this scheme is accepted, many will need to make a major philosophical adjustment. We will also need to learn new content. But then, technology is changing, the world is changing, and education is changing. As a result, we will also need to keep changing.

References

Bensen, M. J. (1979). Clusters or concepts in selecting industrial arts content. *The Journal of Epsilon Pi Tau*.

Bindocci, C. (1983). *Identification of technology content for science and technology centers*. Unpublished doctoral dissertation, West Virginia University, Morgantown, WV.

DeVore, P. W. (1986). *Structure and content foundations for curriculum development*. Reston, VA: American Industrial Arts Association.

DuVall, B., Maughan, G., & Berger, E. (1981). *Getting the message: The technology of communications*. Worcester, MA: Davis Publications.

Davis & McCormack. (1979). *The information age*. Reading, MA: Addison Wesley.

Didsbury, H. F. (1982). *Communications and the future*. Bethesda, MD: The World Future Society.

Face, W. & Flug, E. R. (1966). *The American industry project*. Menomonie, WI: Stout State University.

Forester, T. (1985). *The information technology revolution*. Cambridge, MA: The MIT Press.

Gagne, R. M., & Brigs, L. J. (1974). *Principles of instructional design*. New York: Holt, Rinehart and Winston.

Gray, J. R. (1980). Conceptual attainment in technology: Development of an instructional strategy. *Man/Society/Technology, 40*(2), 21-24.

Halfin, H. H. (1973). *Technology: A process approach*. Unpublished doctoral dissertation. West Virginia University, Morgantown, WV.

Hauenstein, A. D. & Bachmeyer, S. A. (1974). *The world of visual communications*. Bloomington, IL: McKnight & McKnight.

Hendricks, R. W. (1986). *Communication technology: A taxonomy. Unpublished doctoral dissertation*. Ohio State University, Columbus, OH.

Hendricks, R. W. & Sterry, L. F. (1989). *Communication technology*. Menomonie, WI: T & E Publications.

Kranzberg, M. (1967). *Technology in western civilization*. Oxford, England: Oxford University.

Masuda, Y. (1980). *The information society as post-industrial society*. Bethesda, MD: The World Future Society.

Naisbitt, J. (1982). *Megatrends*. New York: Warner Books.

Richter, J. J. (1980). *The construction and partial validation of a scale to measure technological literacy of communication technology*. Unpublished doctoral dissertation. West Virginia University, Morgantown, WV.

Sterry, L. & Wright, T. (1982). *Industry and technology education*. Technical Foundation of America.

Toffler, A. (1980). *The third wave*. New York: Morrow.

Warner, W. E. (1947). A curriculum to reflect technology. *The Journal of Epsilon Pi Tau.*

Chapter 7

SELECTING AND DEVELOPING COMMUNICATION ACTIVITIES

Mark E. Sanders
Associate Professor
Technology Education Program Area
Virginia Polytechnic Institute and State University
Blacksburg, Virginia

Introduction

Technology educators have produced a history rich in "hands-on" instructional activities. Industrial arts educators collectively nodded when John Dewey (1983, p. 13) proclaimed ". . . all genuine education comes about through experiences." The "project method" has been the dominant means of delivering and reinforcing instruction in the field throughout this century.

The shift from manual training to industrial arts in the early part of the century called for a subsequent change in the type of activities used in the classroom. While manual training focused upon the development of specific manual skills, industrial arts took a considerably broader approach to the study of industry. Industrial arts encompassed both the study of how materials were transformed to increase their value, and the "problems of life related to these changes" (Bonser & Mossman, 1923). And with this change in philosophy came a corresponding shift from the "Russian System" to the "project method."

Likewise, the evolution from industrial arts to technology education calls for a new approach to selecting and developing instructional activities. While the profession continues to struggle with its identity and seminal beliefs, most agree the pump lamp no longer has a place in the student activities.

For similar reasons, it is inappropriate to champion letterpress and screen printing as the backbone of the communication program. Letterpress is virtually obsolete, and screen printing accounts for less than 5% of sales in the printing industry. Moreover, "printing" must take its place alongside other technical processes now common to the study of communication systems.

The challenge confronting communication teachers is to transform their curricula to represent more accurately the current technical means of communication. In addition, an obligation exists to portray not only the "evolution, utilization, and significance" of the technical means associated with communication, but also its "organization, resources, products, and accompanying social/cultural impacts" (ITEA, 1985, p. 25). While the author believes this current definition to be nearly identical to Bonser and Mossman's (1923) interpretation of industrial arts, nevertheless it supports the notion of a curriculum overhaul to include the area of communication technology.

How do we, as a profession, go about such a transition? Upon what premises should these new activities be based? Who is to say that one activity is more appropriate than another? In short, what should the "go/no-go gauge" for the selection of activities to teach communication look like?

Unfortunately, the answer is not a simple one. Activities should not be selected "by the seat of the pants" (Bensen, 1980). They should be founded in pedagogical theory and tailored to support the purposes and goals of technology education. Discovering them should not be serendipitous, but rather a calculated process that begins with the development of the appropriate framework.

Developing a Framework
for Activity Selection

As the profession continues to move from industrial arts to technology education, it is imperative that curriculum developers revisit the fundamentals of curriculum design. Sound curriculum designs are not simply a collection of lessons and activities, but rather a calculated set of lessons and activities designed to fulfill effectively the goals common to a given field. For this reason, the purposes and goals of technology education are an appropriate place to begin the search for meaningful activities.

This presents a problem of sorts, as there does not yet appear to be a consensus on the definition, mission, goals, and purposes of technology education. State plans for technology education, for example, differ considerably in their interpretation of these key understandings. Likewise, the definition cited earlier, endorsed by ITEA in 1985, is significantly different from the definition ITEA endorsed in 1988:

"Technology education is the school discipline for the study of the application of knowledge, creativity, and resources to solve problems and extend human potential" (1988, p. 16).

Despite this general lack of consensus, stated purposes for each of the three school levels -- elementary, middle, and secondary -- should serve as useful guidelines for communication teachers. The Technology Education Advisory Council posed the following set of purposes for technology education (ITEA, 1988, pp. 17-20):

Technology education at the elementary level:

-provides an opportunity for children to learn fundamental concepts on how people create and control their environment;

-reinforces and enriches concepts in the sciences, mathematics, language arts, and other subject areas in the elementary school curriculum;

-allows students to work with tools, materials, and technological concepts and processes; and

-develops an awareness of technology.

Students taking technology education at the middle school level will:

-appreciate the scope of contemporary technology;

-safely use basic tools, machines, materials, and processes associated with technology;

-identify occupational fields and educational programs in technological career fields; study and analyze the materials, products' processes, problems, uses, developments, and contributions of these related career fields;

-experience the organization and management systems of business and industry; and

-research, plan, design, construct, and evaluate problems and projects common to technological career fields.

Students at (the high school) level will:

-experience the practical application of basic scientific and mathematical principles;

-make decisions about post-secondary technology careers, engineering programs, or service-related fields;

-make decisions about advanced technical education programs;

-gain an in-depth understanding and appreciation for technology in our society and culture;

-develop basic skill in the use of tools, machines, materials, and processes; and

-solve problems involving the tools, machines, materials, processes, products, and services of industry and technology.

Those reluctant to embrace the move to technology education may be reassured that the aforementioned goals are quite similar to those of industrial arts education (see, for example, Wilber & Pendered, 1973, p. 16). An item-by-item comparison between these two sets of goals suggests a de-emphasis on math and science principles, organization and management systems of industry, and the socio-cultural implications of technology.

Communication teachers should take note of these general goals, as they pertain to the level at which they are working. Technology education should be perceived as an evolution, not a revolution. Communication programs should evolve so as to shift their emphasis gradually: a little less skill development and a little more concern for the implications of the various communication technologies.

It is also important that communication teachers keep these shifting goals in perspective. The goals stated above continue to indicate the importance of traditional goals, such as a basic understanding of the use of tools, machines, materials, and processes of industry and technology. At the same time, they suggest we not overlook the societal implications of technology and the relevance of math and science concepts in our curriculum.

The Domains of Learning

Activities selected for use in communication courses should, first and foremost, satisfy the purposes of technology education. Next, they should be in alignment with the goals and objectives of the communication course. These goals and objectives should be structured around the three domains of learning: psychomotor, cognitive, and affective. We might think of these domains as the "doing," "thinking," and "feeling" aspects of human behavior.

Communication teachers should strive for some sort of a balance among the three domains. It is neither possible nor desirable to demonstrate equal weighting of coursework directed toward each of the three domains, but it is important that one not be emphasized to the point of neglecting one or both of the other two. Technology education is somewhat unique in its ability to represent all three domains comfortably. But, as with all other aspects of the curriculum, it does not happen automatically. Communication teachers should consciously plan their courses and select activities with all three domains in mind.

In practice, the communication laboratory must be a place where students reinforce cognitive understandings with psychomotor activities. Experiential learning must remain the backbone of the program. The shift from the industrial arts to the technology education paradigm must not result in a significant de-emphasis of hands-on activity. For it is this experiential learning that makes technology education unique. Without substantial hands-on activity in the communication laboratory, it might just as well be a science or social studies classroom.

This is not to say we should completely neglect meaningful discussion of socio-cultural implications of communication technologies. Such discussion is important in developing a well-rounded understanding of technology. But, we should continue to emphasize that particular uniqueness our students may bring to this discussion . . . the kinds of understandings that result from actual hands-on experience with a given communication technique. A student who has experienced the ease of facsimile transmission may better appreciate the dilemma of "fax junk mail" than one who has only engaged in a general discussion (with or without overhead transparencies) of the concept of facsimile transmission.

Hands-on activities must be complemented with activities that reinforce cognitive understanding. There is a wealth of information relating to "how communication works" that must be addressed in the communication program. In order to comprehend telecommunication among computers, for example, a student must have a reasonable understanding of digital systems. The concepts of sender, channel, and receiver, as well as the business of bits, bytes, ASCII character code, serial and parallel data transfer, etc., are all important parts of the puzzle. To deprive students of activities that reinforce these aspects of the telecommunication process radically limits their understanding of the process. This portion of the learning process is vitally important when something "goes wrong." Trouble shooting (problem solving) is often a "gestalting" process, in which the solution is derived collectively from the sum total of prior knowledge. If this knowledge is limited primarily to a hands-on activity that was guided by a step-by-step procedure sheet, you may expect little or no "gestalting" to take place.

Likewise, communication teachers must be careful not to overemphasize the psychomotor domain. This approach can quickly lead to a quasi-vocational program in which skill level becomes the objective, rather than conceptual understanding of the technology. Activities aimed at skill proficiency through continuous repetition should be avoided. This sort of emphasis is not consistent with the goals and purposes of technology education. Similarly, communication teachers must be cautious not to select activities on the basis of occupational analysis. The curriculum must remain a broad orientation and include a wide range of activities, rather than focus on specific job entry skills.

Laboratory-based activities in communication technology and systems lend themselves to the affective domain as well. Activities should be selected to increase the students' chances of succeeding in their work. There is almost nothing more important to adolescent or pre-adolescent students than their self-concept. And nothing builds a positive self-concept better than success, no matter what the arena. Group activities foster affective behaviors, such as cooperation, responsibility, and leadership. With some forethought, communication activities may be designed to promote desirable affective behaviors.

Learning Theory

The literature and research relating to how children learn is of critical importance to those designing technology education curricula. There are many practical applications of learning theory that are too often overlooked in the classroom.

Taba (1962, pp. 79-82) identifies three general theories of learning: faculty psychology, behaviorism, and Gestalt theory. Those who subscribe to the theory of faculty psychology believe the mind contains all the necessary "faculties," and the purpose of education is simply to bring these out with learning exercises. The mind is treated like a muscle. The more difficult the learning exercise, the better . . . no pain, no gain.

Behaviorist theory suggests the mind contains a collection of responses, which manifest when triggered by specific stimuli. Proponents of this model believe learning takes place by associating responses with their stimuli. This "conditioning" may be encouraged with positive or negative reinforcement.

Gestalt and related "field theories" picture the human mind as an organizer of previous experience and cognition. All perception is recorded in memory, creating a cognitive structure. New perceptions are processed relative to this cognitive structure; that is, learning is an active process of selecting from and reorganizing this cognitive map. At times, this selecting/reorganizing results in a new insight -- an intuitive leap fueled by prior experience.

To some extent, elements of each of these general theories of learning filter into technology education curricula. Faculty psychology, the theory that best supports the notion of studying difficult subjects such as Latin and mathematics, has the least relevance for communication programs. The stimulus-response tenet of behaviorism, on the other hand, may be observed in the normal course of many activities in the communication program. Novice computer users, for example, learn that computers are not the cause of most of their problems. They come to realize, through conditioning, that the strange things that seem to happen are, for the most part, the direct result of a minor error on their part. Often by trial and error (conditioning), they learn to avoid certain procedures (stimuli) that result in unwanted responses.

Curricula based on behavioristic principles are highly structured, as they attempt to associate specific responses with set stimuli. The emphasis is on memorization. Specific content, rather than general principles or ideas, are at the center of the curriculum. The job analysis method of curriculum development (Bobbitt, 1924; Charters, 1938), historically used by vocational programs, incorporates many of the principles of behaviorism.

The stimulus/response concept of learning, however, presumes the mind to be passive. High-level thinking takes a back seat to the more fundamental process of association. Therefore, this model is better suited to the purposes of the manual training movement in the early part of the century than to the objectives of technology education.

Problem solving and "systems approaches" are recurring themes in technology education. Communication programs designed with these approaches in mind, will strive to provide greater emphasis on general principles and creative intuition than in the past. As this happens, the field will find itself more and more ensconced in the principles of field theory . . . the Gestalt.

Theory into Practice:
Some Helpful Suggestions

While the foundations of learning theory are arguably obtuse, a substantial number of concrete recommendations have been filtered out over the years. As communication teachers go about the process of selecting activities, they would do well to consult sources of practical suggestions, a number of which are cited on the next page.

Hilgard (1956, pp. 486-487) identified fourteen basic principles of learning:

1. The capacity of the learner is vitally important (intelligence and age of the learner, for example, are relevant considerations).
2. Motivated students learn more rapidly than unmotivated ones.
3. Excessive motivation (fear and anxiety) may inhibit, rather than foster, the learning process. Moderate motivation works best.
4. Intrinsic motivation works better than extrinsic motivation.
5. Reward generally works better than punishment; success works better than failure.
6. A history of repeated success is the best way to develop a tolerance for failure.
7. Realistic goals are important, and students may learn to set realistic goals through practice.
8. A student's personality traits may hinder his/her ability to learn from a given teacher.
9. Active participation works better than passive learning.
10. Meaningful tasks are learned more rapidly than nonmeaningful activities.
11. There is no substitute for repetitive practice in learning a psychomotor skill or memorizing unrelated facts.
12. Feedback and evaluation aid in the learning process.
13. Transfer of learning to new tasks will be better if the learners discover relationships on their own and may apply them within a variety of tasks.
14. Distributed recall fosters long-term memory.

Hilgard's suggestions appear as common threads throughout all pedagogy. The key issues identified are: learner motivation, readiness, success, relevance, positive reinforcement, feedback, practice, self discovery, and active participation. No competent educator would deny their importance in any curriculum. Indeed, cliches such as "Nothing breeds success like success" and "practice makes perfect" may be inferred from Hilgard's list.

Exemplary teachers, in fact, view these ideas as somewhat ordinary, yet they are the "stuff" of which quality teaching is made. Most of them presume a preassessment of student demographics; something that no state or national curriculum which includes communication technology will ever be able to do. Activity selection, in the final analysis, is within the domain of the classroom teacher. To be effective, therefore, communication teachers must revisit these curriculum "basics" as they select activities to support their instruction.

Tyler (1949) identified three criteria for organizing learning experiences: continuity, sequence, and integration. "Continuity" was Tyler's way of suggesting that important skills, such as reading, should be practiced over and over again. In Tyler's words, "if an objective of science is to develop a meaningful concept of energy, it is important that this concept be dealt with again and again in various parts of the science course" (p. 84). The same might be said of the concept of "encoding" for communication teachers. For it to make any sense, it will have to be reiterated and supported with activities time and again throughout the program.

Tyler's concept of "sequence" suggested that all experiences should build upon earlier experiences. This is an extension of continuity--as experiences are revisited (continuity), there should be a gradual expansion of the breadth, depth, and complexity of the experience, for meaningful learning to occur. Encoding graphic images for printing, for example, is less complex than encoding a message for electromagnetic communication. It makes sense to grasp the former before tackling the latter.

"Integration" stresses the importance of one topic to another. It is critical that students see horizontal relationships among ideas. As he put it, "In developing skill in handling quantitative problems in arithmetic, it is also important to consider the ways in which these skills can be effectively utilized in social studies, in science, in shop, and in other fields so that they are not developed simply as isolated behaviors . . . ." This, of course, works both ways. Communication teachers should relate the concepts and practices studied in the communication laboratory to those dealt with in other subjects. The production of a school's literary/arts magazine, for which the writing and illustration are done in the English and art classes respectively, goes a long way toward accomplishing this objective. It's simply a question of isolation versus integration. Not only will integrated activities "work" better, they are also excellent means of fostering respect for our discipline throughout the school and community.

Even more specifically, Tyler identified five principles for selecting activities:

1. For a given objective to be attained, a student must have experiences that give him an opportunity to practice the kind of behavior implied by the objective.
2. The learning experience must be such that the student obtains satisfaction from carrying on the kind of behavior implied by the objectives.

123

3. The reactions desired in the experiences are within the range of possibility for the students involved.
4. There are many particular experiences that can be used to attain the same educational objective.
5. The same learning experience will usually bring about several outcomes (pp. 66-67).

Bruner (1960) dealt with many of the same issues. He categorized his concerns into four general themes:

1. The role of structure in learning: horizontal relationships among concepts is critical.
2. The readiness for learning: any subject may be taught to anyone at any age if that subject is appropriately tailored.
3. The nature of intuition: we can teach the gift of the "shrewd" guess, the fertile hypothesis, the courageous leap to a tentative conclusion.
4. Motivation: "The quest . . . is to devise materials that will challenge the superior student while not destroying the confidence and will-to-learn of those who are less fortunate."

A substantial body of research on personality and learning styles has enormous implications for curriculum development and activity selection. Specifically, the work of Carl Jung and Isabel Briggs Myers is highly relevant. Jung (1953) developed a classification scheme for cognitive processing and "psychological types." Isabel Briggs Myers, a self-taught psychologist, collected data on personality types throughout the 1950's and 1960's. She identified sixteen different personality types and published the Myers-Briggs Type Indicator (1962), an instrument used to assess personality type.

Myer's personality research has obvious implications for the teaching/learning process. She classified all learners as either "intuitive" or "sensing" types. As she explains: "Intuitives and sensing types differ greatly in what they find interesting in any subject. . . . Intuitives like the principle, the theory, the why. Sensing types like the practical application, the what, and the how" (1980, p. 154). The relevance of her point is driven home by her further explanation, "Most subjects have both theoretical and practical aspects and can be taught with the emphasis on either" (p. 154).

Communication teachers are in an opportunistic position to capitalize on these realities. Because we work in laboratory settings, we have the chance to reach both sensing and intuitive types effectively. Most people will learn more during a one-hour demonstration of a page layout program such as "PageMaker" than from dozens of hours reading reams of "desktop publishing" articles. And those who go so far as to spend an hour of hands-on activity with the software will-develop a conceptual understanding that can never be achieved via other means.

Myers' work stimulated a plethora of research in the area of personality type and its implications for the teaching/learning process. Practical treatises on the application of her findings in education include her own (Myers, 1980) and those by Lawrence (1979), and McCaulley and Natter (1974), to name but a few. In addition, the Center for the Applications of Psychological Type and the journal entitled *Research in Psychological Types* report the findings of a wide range of related research.

A substantial volume of research focuses on the concept of human development and is of interest to educational psychologists and practitioners: physical, social, emotional, and mental. Piaget (1950, pp. 87-158) described three distinct stages of cognitive development in young children: sensimotor, concrete operations, and conceptual thought. The third phase, conceptual thought, normally occurs between eleven years and adolescence. Prior to this stage of development, children are only capable of seeing abstract relationships in terms of concrete objects present in the immediate environment. Not until the conceptual thought stage (after age eleven) do they become adept at conceptual problem solving: posing hypotheses and developing solutions through synthesis of ideas rather than objects in the immediate environment.

Havighurst (1953) identified "developmental tasks" that occur at specific times in life. The many specific tasks he identified were grouped into infancy and early childhood, middle childhood, adolescence, early adulthood, middle age, and later maturity.

The body of developmental research fostered a range of theories regarding readiness for learning and pacing. Hilgard (1957, pp. 60-63) provided four guidelines on pacing:

1. Skills that build upon developing behavior are most easily learned.
2. The more mature the organism, the less training is needed to reach a given level of proficiency.
3. Training given before the maturational readiness may bring either no improvement, or only temporary improvement.
4. Premature training, if frustrating, may do more harm than good.

There is general agreement in the literature that pacing and readiness are important factors in determining curriculum. But, readiness is not determined by human development alone. Prior experience is also of critical importance, and includes experiences gained in the classroom. That is, readiness is as much a function of prior classroom experience as it is a function of the human maturation process (Ausubel, 1967). Gagne's (1965) notion of learning "hierarchies" and Taba's (1967), "spiral curriculum" are other manifestations of the notions of pacing and readiness applied to the curriculum.

Curriculum Designs

Curriculum designers in technology education, communication teachers among them, ultimately must pull together content and learning activities to create the courses that make up their programs. These efforts should obviously build upon the aforementioned pedagogy. There is, however, no single way of going about this task.

A number of educational researchers have analyzed curricula and found similarities among them (see, for example, Eisner and Vallance, 1974; McNeil, 1977; Eisner, 1979; Joyce,1980; Saylor and Alexander, 1981; Wiles and Bondi, 1984; Schubert, 1985; and Ornstein and Hunkins, 1988). These researchers were able to categorize the different curricula into three to seven different curriculum "orientations."

Zuga, et al (1989, pp. 14-20), examined each of these curriculum orientations and grouped them according to five primary foci: academic, technical, intellectual processes, social, and personal. These foci parallel those suggested by Eisner and Vallance (1974). Zuga's description of these five curriculum orientations is summarized below, along with examples from the field of technology education that help to illustrate each.

Academic. The academic orientation focuses on a set body of knowledge grouped in disciplines, subject matter, or broad fields.

DeVore's (1964) discussion of a taxonometric structure for the discipline of technology that paralleled those of the sciences is an example of the academic approach to curriculum design.

In technology education, there is an increasing emphasis on the academic curriculum model. Towers, Lux, and Ray (1966) developed a structure of knowledge for industrial technology that has clearly been incorporated into many curriculum models now under the technology education umbrella. McCrory (1980) built upon DeVore's discussion of the need for a taxonomy for the discipline of technology. Hendricks' (1987) taxonomy for communication technology provides support for subsequent application of the academic design to curriculum development in the communication cluster.

Technical. Technical curriculum designs are based upon the analysis of learner performance on tasks. These designs rely upon a technological approach to the design process, such as task analysis or the systematic development of goals, objectives, and behavioral outcomes.

This design is easily the most prevalent in technology education curricula today. Virtually all of the state-developed communication technology guides were structured around goals, objectives, and behavioral outcomes. This is due, to a large extent, to the influence of behavioral psychology on education throughout most of this century. Ritz (1980, pp. 11-13), for example, proposed a technical curriculum planning process based on his analysis of various technical models.

There has also been some spillover into technology education of the job and task analysis and competency-based instructional models used by trade and industrial and other vocational programs. These, however, are highly inappropriate for technology education. They reduce the teaching/learning process to a series of mindless steps and hurdles, guaranteeing a degree of psychomotor competence rather than fostering the acquisition of concepts. They are suitable models for technical training, but have little place in the general education curriculum.

Intellectual Processes. Intellectual processes focus on the development of cognitive processes, such as critical thinking and problem solving, or on human traits, such as creativity and self confidence. These processes are taught within the context of the subject matter content, but the intellectual processes remain the focus of the curriculum, not the content.

There are few, if any, pure applications of this model in technology education. Perhaps the closest approximation is embodied by the Olympics of the Mind philosophy (OM Association, 1987), though OM is an extracurricular activity, rather than a curriculum design. Wey (1985) developed a guidebook for teaching creativity that fits nicely into the intellectual processes model. Approaches promoted by Sarapin and Starkweather (1981) and Hatch (1988) also embody many of the principles of this design. Substantial dialogue in the profession regarding the relevance of problem solving may foster increased reliance on the intellectual processes orientation in the future.

Social. Social curriculum designs center on the application of knowledge in real-world situations. The curriculum is structured around the notion of students as future agents of change in society (social reconstruction), or the idea of students fitting into society (social adaptation). In either case, the social context is of paramount importance in this curriculum design.

As with the intellectual processes design, there are few examples of this approach to curriculum in technology education. Pytlik (1981) proposed a new technology course entitled "Human Values in Science and Technology" that incorporated elements of the social design. The increasing emphasis on the teaching of the social implications of technology (see, for example, Wright, 1988) suggests an increasing interest in the social curriculum design in technology education.

Personal. Personal curriculum designs focus on the needs and interests of the learner. Unlike other designs, personal curriculum designs evolve from the student rather than the teacher. Content is student driven; that is, students are encouraged, in these models, to make decisions regarding the material they study within the general constraints of the subject being studied. The Maryland Plan (Maley, 1973) is a manifestation of the personal curriculum design. Moss (1987) also argues the case for a student-centered technology education curriculum.

Practical Assumptions and Limitations

In the best of all worlds, curriculum planning and activity selection would be driven solely by the sound guidelines established by the learning theory and the principles of pedagogy. In reality, however, there is a matrix of assumptions and limitations which temper the process of activity selection.

Among the most significant of these is teacher expertise. Few would argue the truth of the adage, "We teach as we have been taught." A corollary to this might be, "We teach what we know." And, what we know is often what we have been taught.

This poses a problem for communication teachers, because communication technologies change so rapidly. A communication teacher who does not spend a substantial amount of time (perhaps as much as one full day a week) keeping up with the techniques of communication, simply cannot remain abreast of the changes. Of course, there are obvious limitations on any teacher's time. Because few teachers receive adequate support for professional development, the only way to spend an adequate amount of time keeping up is to do it beyond the normal working day. That means dedicating nights, weekends, and summers to the ongoing task of maintaining technical competence.

The "Resources" and "Strategies" sections of this chapter offer some suggestions in this area. The unfortunate reality, however, is that much of this is "out of hide" time for the teacher. As most of us know, the best teachers are those who work at it "round-the-clock." That goes for all disciplines, not just technology education.

A related limitation is the communication teacher's personal perspective and philosophy. That perspective is a complex amalgamation of previous experiences and is not likely to be readily altered. Many inservice communication teachers, for example, are former "printing," "drafting," or "electronics" teachers. It may be difficult for them to move from one of these mindsets to a more broadly based "communication" perspective.

Change of this sort is more likely to be evolutionary rather than revolutionary. Frankly, if a teacher is highly successful with his/her current curriculum, there is little motivation to change. This fact alone helps to explain the reluctance of many teachers to make wholesale changes in the courses they teach.

In order for teachers to adopt new curricula programs and courses, they must first be convinced that the new way is somehow better than the old way. Drafting teachers who experience the "power" of CAD for the first time are generally eager to incorporate CAD into their courses. The benefits are easy to see. The same is true of computer aided publishing for a printing teacher. This is the place to start. If these teachers see similar advantages to a broad approach to the area of communication, they may be enticed to expand their limited approach to include such areas as audio and video communication.

Another obvious limitation is that of local facilities and financial resources. Communication activities, for the most part, require facilities. Talk is cheap, which is why it is so often the predominant means of instruction; but, lecture alone will not suffice for a communication teacher. As noted earlier, hands-on activities are absolutely essential.

Communication teachers can solve many of their facility and resource problems by constantly lobbying for their cause. Sanders (1984) found that about nine out of ten graphic communication teachers requesting support from local industries received materials and equipment for their efforts. Likewise, local school administrators are often receptive to well-thought-out proposals for support. Just as keeping abreast of the technology requires constant effort, gaining support for upgrading facilities requires continual work. Communication teachers must remember that the majority of funding for the education enterprise is local, not from state or federal sources.

Finally, the external influences, such as school administration and community personnel, often play a disproportionate role in shaping the curriculum. In many cases, school administrators and guidance personnel maintain a perception of "industrial arts shops" as a place intended solely for the mainstreaming of learning disabled and special needs students. Traditionally, industrial arts often did more for these students than any other curriculum in school. However, technology education has an important role to play for all students in the school, and it is absolutely critical that administrators and guidance personnel be educated along these lines. Otherwise, the process of curriculum development/activity selection defaults to the traditional industrial arts approach in order to meet the expectations of those outside the discipline.

Likewise, community expectations sometimes drive the curriculum. When communication teachers set up advisory committees, they run this distinct risk. They must be careful not to let the tail wag the dog.

Analyzing Existing Activities

An important stage of curriculum development for communication teachers is to analyze their current activities to see if they, in fact, measure up. Each activity must be examined in light of the pedagogical and pragmatic concerns discussed thus far. The following checklist is a good place to start:

1. Does the activity support the goals and objectives of technology education, and more specifically, communication technology?
2. Do the activities collectively represent the three domains of learning: psychomotor, cognitive, and affective?
3. Is the activity representative of current communication technologies and explore communication systems?
4. Are the knowledge base and previous experiences of the students in the communication course such that one might expect them to be successful in working with a given activity?
5. Does the activity build upon (and go beyond) previous learning?
6. Does the activity integrate with concepts and principles taught in other curricula?
7. Will the activity be meaningful to the students and self-motivating?
8. Is there a way to adequately provide feedback and evaluate student performance for the activity?

9. Is there ample opportunity for students to discover relationships and solutions on their own?
10. Is there enough variability among activities so as to suit different learning styles?

To the extent that existing activities fit within the context of these guidelines, they should be retained. In cases where they do not meet these criteria, they should be modified or purged from the communication program. Generally, this sort of obsolescence is easiest to judge with respect to criterion #3. Since letterpress printing, for example, is virtually obsolete, it makes sense to remove letterpress activities from the communication coursework. The same rigor should be applied with regard to the other criteria in the list. An activity that students find frustrating, for example, does a disservice to students if it yields more failure and frustration than success, and should, therefore, be removed.

When evaluating new activities, communication teachers should also measure prospective activities against the above list. In addition, there are other practical considerations:

1. Is the activity "do-able" given the facilities and resources of the program? Or, can new means of support be located for the activity?
2. Does the instructor have the requisite knowledge to successfully manage the activity?

Strategies for Selecting Communication Activities

The best teachers constantly seek new activities to improve their program, particularly when the content base is as dynamic as technology. Not only is there continuous innovation in the area of communication, but there is considerable invention as well. Fortunately, there are plenty of sources a communication teacher may scout for new activities. In fact, there are more potential activities "out there" than we might hope to incorporate into any communication program. Identifying these is the easy part. The real problem is discriminating among the universe of possible activities to narrow the list to those that will most meaningfully support the technology education curriculum.

Given the five orientations to curriculum design discussed earlier, it should be evident that there is no one best way to go about this process. Different teachers will want to approach the problem from different directions.

Those who fit the "academic" orientation will likely want to zero in on a taxonomy of communication concepts (Hendricks, 1987) as a starting point. This approach would suggest they look for activities that reinforce the concepts of encoding, transmitting, receiving, storing, retrieving, decoding, and feedback.

Teachers who prefer the "technological" orientation of curriculum design (this includes most technology teachers) would more likely diagnose needs, formulate general and specific course objectives, and then select content. Activities would then be selected which directly support the specific course objectives developed under this approach (Taba, 1962).

Those who favor an "intellectual processes" design would seek to determine the important cognitive processes. These processes, rather than the processes of communication, would drive the curriculum and activity selection. Communication activities would be selected that best reinforced the cognitive processes deemed most important, such as creativity, problem solving, critical thinking, and so forth.

In the best of all worlds, curriculum design and course construction would proceed logically and methodically, guided by many of the pedagogical fundamentals discussed earlier in this chapter. In reality, teachers generally have precious little time to contemplate the problem of curriculum development. Indeed, research suggests many teachers do not approach curriculum development in this fashion.

Zuga, LaPorte, Scott, and Liang (1989, pp. 31-32) and Bensen (1980, p. 12) found that technology teachers typically identified activities they believed would motivate their students, and then developed the course objectives to justify those activities. While this flies in the face of curriculum development theory, it, nevertheless, may be the predominant practice.

Every good teacher knows that motivation is at the heart of all learning. This simply means that when motivation is the primary consideration in activity selection, content is less significant. It suggests a greater reliance on the "personal" orientation to curriculum design than the "technical" or "academic" orientations that dominate the thinking of the majority of curriculum theorists.

This bothers many in the field of technology education, because the predominant curriculum orientation has been the technical design. Communication teachers who build their program by beginning with motivation activities (perhaps the great majority) would do well to evaluate those activities according to criteria #2-10 identified in the "Analyzing Existing Activities" section of this chapter. Despite having bypassed criterion #1, they might be more confident that the activities not only motivate, but are educationally sound.

In scanning the horizons for suitable communication activities communication teachers should concentrate their search on the "basic" concepts and processes . . . not the exotic ones. The "picture phone" may seem more interesting than the telephone that you have on your desk, but the latter is far more appropriate as an area of study for the communication curriculum than the former. There is some danger in bypassing the "basic" communication technologies in favor of the more innovative.

The field of technology education seems enamored with these new technologies, without any real consideration for how they fit into the curriculum. Many believe that a communication technology program with "show and tell" units on fiber optics and lasers is automatically light-years ahead of the program that chooses to use that time for teaching the fundamentals of photography and printing. This is not necessarily the case; there is no research to suggest a smorgasbord of sexy new technologies is a better way to teach communication technology than a systematic introduction to the "basic" communication technologies.

A related problem is the perception that technologies such as desktop publishing are new and unique to technology education. In reality, computer aided publishing (a more appropriate term for the concept of using computers to assist in the publication process) is simply a logical extension of the "graphic arts" or "graphic communication" curriculum. Computer-based composition has existed for three decades. "Desktop publishing" is simply the latest twist. All of the basic understandings essential to what is now known as "desktop publishing" were traditionally taught in our "graphic arts" classes.

Communication activities should cover the spectrum of communication content. Specifically, activities should be selected which represent the major components of communication technology -- graphic production systems, technical design systems, data communication systems, optic systems, and audio and video communication systems -- these serve as one means to organize content. Once introductory content and activities have been covered in each of these areas, it is appropriate to move to more exotic applications. In the area of optic systems, for example, photography should precede holography. Holography is an excellent way to teach the application of optics and lasers. But the principles of optics may be learned more easily from photography, and in the grand scheme of communication technology, photography is vastly more significant than holography.

After all of the seminal understanding (basics) from each of the five component areas noted above have been adequately provided for in the curriculum, the communication teacher is at liberty to weave in more exotic applications. Rather than concentrate on one particular component, the curriculum would better suit the purposes of technology education if it included all five of the areas. The program that ignores the fundamentals of graphic production systems (printing), for example, and instead has three courses in technical design, is more representative of a vocational trade and industry curriculum than a technology education program.

A final strategy to consider when selecting communication activities relates to the emphasis of that activity. The emphasis of activities selected for technology education programs should be on technological applications. Teaching about lasers by setting one up and measuring the divergence of the beam is the wrong approach. This is what science teachers should be doing with lasers. This sort of activity focuses on the scientific principle, not the application of the scientific principle. Communication technology teachers would do better by making a hologram with the laser. Just as photography is the application of optic principles, holography is the application of laser principles. It is more the domain of the technology teacher than that of the science teacher. The scientific principles should not be ignored in the technology education laboratory, but they must not be the primary objective of the activity. The primary criterion for selecting an activity should be that it demonstrates an application of the scientific principle.

Resources for Communication Activities

Generating the list of potential activities from which to select is a fairly simple process. There are a large number of sources for communication activity ideas. Communication teachers should consider the following types of sources.

Textbooks. There are five textbooks currently available on communication technology: (Hacker, 1989; Hendricks & Sterry, 1987; Jones & Robb, 1987; Ritz, Seymour, & Cloughessy, 1988; and Sanders, 1990). These cover much the same content: graphic production, technical design, optic audio and video, and data communication systems. Specific activities are suggested in these texts, as well as in their accompanying student manuals.

State Curriculum Guides. Many states have curriculum guides that list a substantial number of good activities.

Communication Trade and Popular Literature. There is a vast amount of trade literature in the communication field and related technical fields, most of which is free to teachers. A brief sampling might include the following.

Graphic Production Systems. *Graphic Arts Monthly, Quick Printing, Electronic Printing and Publishing, American Printer, Screen Printing, Gravure, Flexo,* (or consult the Graphic Arts Technical Foundation's Abstracts for a comprehensive listing).

Technical Design Systems. *Design Graphics World, Plan and Print,* and *Design Engineering.*

Optic Systems. *Popular Photography, Technical Photography, Peterson's Photographic, Modern Photography, Darkroom,* and *Electronic Imaging.*

Audio and Video Systems. *E & I TV, Media Methods, Audio Video Communication, Audio-visual, Radio Electronics, Audio,* and *EPIE Report.*

Data Communication Systems. *PC, A+, MacUser, Publish, ITC Desktop, MacWorld, True Imaging, Electronic Learning,* and *The Journal.*

Technology Education Literature. Communication activity ideas appear in professional publications such as *The Technology Teacher, School Shop, Industrial Education,* and the *Visual Communications Journal.*

Conferences. A wide range of conferences that relate to communication are held by various organizations. A brief listing might include the annual conferences of the following associations: International Graphic Arts Education Association, International Technology Education Association, National Computer Graphics Association, Association for Educational Computing Technologies, and state and regional Technology Education conferences and meetings, to name but a few.

Other Communication Teachers. Why reinvent the wheel? Other communication teachers are an excellent source of ideas. They may be found, en masse, at the national and state educational conferences noted above, as well as at local gatherings of technology teachers.

Industry and Corporate Analysis. Most of what the technology education literature suggests we teach relates directly to business and industry. An analysis of the concepts and processes utilized in the audio, video, technical design, optic, graphic production, and data communication sectors provides a rich source of ideas for communication activities.

References

American Industrial Arts Association. (1985). *Technology education: A perspective on implementation.* Reston, VA.

Ausubel, D. P. (1967). *Learning theory and classroom practice.* New York: Holt, Rinehart, and Winston.

Bensen, M. J. (1980). *Selecting content for technology education.* Symposium '80 Proceedings. Charleston, IL: Eastern Illinois University.

Bobbitt, J. F. (1924). *How to make a curriculum.* Boston, MA: Houghton Mifflin Company.

Bonser, F. G. & Mossman, L. C. (1923). *Industrial arts for elementary schools.* New York: Macmillan Publishing.

Bruner, J. S. (1960). *The process of education.* New York: Random House.

Charters, W. W. (1923). *Curriculum construction.* New York: Macmillan Publishing.

Dewey, J. (1938). *Experience and education.* New York: Macmillan Publishing.

DeVore, P. W. (1964). *Technology as an intellectual discipline.* Bulletin No. 5, Washington, DC: American Industrial Arts Association.

Eisner, E. W. (1979). *The education imagination.* New York: Macmillan Publishing.

Eisner, E. W. & Vallance, E. (1974). *Conflicting conceptions of curriculum.* Berkeley, CA: McCutchan.

Gagne, R. M. (1965). *Conditions of learning.* New York: Holt, Rinehart, & Winston.

Gow, D. T. & Casey, T. W., (Eds.). (1983). *Fundamental curriculum decisions.* Washington, DC: Association for Supervision and Curriculum Development.

Hacker, M. (1989). *Communication technology.* Albany, NY: Delmar.

Hatch, L. (1988). Problem solving approach. *Instruction strategies for technology education,* 37th Yearbook, the Council on Technology Teacher Education.

Havighurst, R. J. (1953). *Human development and education.* New York: Longman.

Hendricks, R. W. (1987). A taxonomy of the concepts of communications technology. In Hendricks, R. W. & Sterry, L. F. *Communication technology.* Menomonie, WI: T & E Publications.

Hilgard, E. R. (1956). *Theories of learning.* New York: Appelton-Centry-Crofts.

Hilgard, E. R. (1957). *Introduction to psychology.* New York: Harcourt, Brace, & World.

International Technology Education Association. (1988). *Technology: A national imperative.* Reston, VA.

Jones, R. E. & Robb, J. L. (1986). *Discovering technology: Communication.* Chicago, IL: Harcourt Brace Jovanovich.

Joyce, B. R. (1980). Learning how to learn. *Theory and practice, 19*(1), 15-27.

Jung, C. (1953). *Psychological types.* New York: Harcourt, Brace, and World.

Lawrence, G. (1979). *People's types and tiger stripes.* Gainesville, FL: Center for Applications of Psychological Type.

Maley, D. (1973). *The Maryland plan*. New York: Bruce.

McCaulley, M. H. & Natter, F. L. (1974). *Psychological (Myers-Briggs) type differences in education*. Gainesville, FL: Center for Applications of Psychological Type.

McCrory, D. L. (1980). Content structure for technology education: Toward new curricula for the 1980's. *The Journal of Epsilon Pi Tau, (6)2*, 27-34.

McNeil, J. D. (1977). *Curriculum: A comprehensive introduction*. Boston, MA: Little Brown.

Moss, J., Jr. (1987). Technology education: Subject- or student-centered? *The Journal of Epsilon Pi Tau, 13*(1), 40-43.

Myers, I. B. (1962). *Introduction to type*. Gainesville, FL: Center for Applications of Psychological Type.

Myers, I. B. (1980). *Gifts differing*. Palo Alto, CA: Consulting Psychologists Press.

OM Association. (1987). *Curriculum materials: Teaching strategies*. Glassboro, NJ: OM Association.

Ornstein, A. C. & Hunkins, F. P. (1988). *Curriculum: Foundations, principles, and issues*. Englewood, NJ: Prentice-Hall.

Piaget, J. (1950). *The psychology of intelligence*. New York: Harcourt, Brace, & World.

Pytlik, E. C. (1981). Technology education and human values: A course for high school students. *The Journal of Epsilon Pi Tau, 7*(2), 36-42.

Ritz, J. M. (1980). Systematic curriculum development for industrial education. *Man/Society/Technology, 40*(1), 11-13.

Ritz, J. M., Seymour, R. D., & Cloughessy, F. A. (1988). *Exploring communication*. South Holland, IL: The Goodheart-Wilcox Co., Inc.

Sanders, M. E. (1984). A national assessment of industrial arts graphic communication programs. *Journal of Industrial Teacher Education, 21*(4), 43-54.

Sanders, M. E. (1990). *Communication technology*. Peoria, IL: Glencoe Publishing.

Sarapin, M. I. & Starkweather, K. N. (1981). Curriculum development: Placing the learner at the center of the instructional process. *The Journal of Epsilon Pi Tau, 7*(1), 60-66.

Saylor, J. G., Alexander, W. M., & Lewis, A. J. (1981). *Curriculum planning: For better teaching and learning*. New York: Holt, Rinehart, and Winston.

Schubert, W. H. (1986). *Curriculum: Perspective, paradigm, and possibility*. New York: Macmillan Publishing.

Taba, H. (1962). *Curriculum development: Theory and practice*. New York: Harcourt, Brace, & World.

Towers, E. R., Lux, D. G., & Ray, W. E. (1966). *A rationale and structure of industrial arts subject matter*. (ERIC Document Reproduction Service No. ED 013 955).

Tyler, R. W. (1949). *Basic principles of curriculum and instruction*. Chicago, IL: University of Chicago.

Wey, B. (1985). Development of a guidebook to promote creativity in industrial education classes. *Journal of Industrial Teacher Education, 22*(3), 37-47.

Selecting and Developing Communication Activities

Wilber, G. O. & Pendered, N. C. (1973). *Industrial arts in general education.* Scranton, PA: International Textbooks.
Wiles, J. & Bondi, J. C. (1984). *Curriculum development: A guide to practice.* Columbus, OH: Bell and Howell.
Wright, J. R. (1988). Social/cultural approach. *Instructional strategies for technology education,* 37th Yearbook, Council of Technology Teacher Education.
Zuga, K. F., LaPorte, J. E., Scott, M., & Liang, T. (1989). *A rationale for designing and testing curriculum planning models for technology education.* Washington, DC: Office of Vocational and Adult Education.

Chapter 8

ESTABLISHING THE COMMUNICATION TEACHING AND LEARNING ENVIRONMENT

Ryan Brown
Assistant Professor
Department of Industrial Technology
Illinois State University
Normal, Illinois

Laboratories and Classrooms for Teaching Communication Technology

Information technology demands a new and fresh approach to the study of communication technologies. Instructors of communication technologies are challenged to provide an education in a vast field of knowledge that may encompass several traditional skills areas, but also includes the study of many exciting new phases of communication. Therefore, design of laboratories and classrooms for teaching communication technology will demand the attention of educational leaders in the years ahead.

These laboratories must house the tools, materials, and resources for activities that will allow students to test, analyze, experiment, read about, investigate, demonstrate, construct, observe, research, and display theories and principles of communication. These laboratories must also facilitate a variety of instructional methods to provide students with experiences in communication systems through creative problem solving, computer networks and interfaces, media creations, and electronic explorations.

Evaluating the Potential of a Facility for Teaching Communication Technology

In the analysis of the facilities that housed traditional industrial education programs or that now are the facilities for technology education programs, a mix of layouts and ideas remains prevalent.

Traditionally, larger schools have had several shops or laboratories, each serving a specific form of learning and instruction. Drafting laboratories, for example, were arranged with several tables, each equipped with a drafting machine or drawing board space. The instructional area provided for demonstrations, and the student area provided for the completion of exercises. Yet, while serving the needs of teaching drafting skills, as in preparing one to be a drafter, the room itself may have been useful for little else. Even the use of computer-assisted drafting workstations has presented problems for the facility planner attempting to retrofit a facility designed for traditional equipment and methods.

Gemmill (1989) outlined and compared the unit shops of years past with current "laboratories of technologies." Gemmill summarized that the equipment and organization of the facilities have changed as a result of technological and pedagogical advancements, but the intent of the laboratory types has remained consistent (p. 2). Utilizing this terminology, unit laboratories are those that provide for specialized areas of technology education, such as computer-aided drafting and design, or photography, or electronic systems, whereas limited general laboratories are used for related groups of technologies such as communication. At the earlier levels of education, a comprehensive general laboratory is appropriate for basic exploratory courses of all phases of technology education.

The potential of a facility for communication technology will be enhanced by its potential to become and remain a safe, secure, and flexible teaching and learning environment. Even the instruction of any one area of communication technology in a single room demands careful planning to ensure utilization of the laboratory to its full potential. As technologies change, the laboratory must be amenable to rearrangement and design. For example, facility and environmental planners of the 1970's were not aware of the desktop computer phenomenon of the 1980's. How can technology education program planners even imagine the environment of the year 2000? The realistic approach calls for modifiable arrangements. In the communications environment alone, connections for computers, modems, cable television, telephone, FAX machines, and many various peripherals require prior thought and planning.

In addition to flexibility, safety remains a factor of the communications technology environment. Although not as "heavy equipment-oriented" as the manufacturing area, there are a variety of tools and equipment that demand proper working environments, safe travel aisles nearby, and perhaps safe storage. Electrical devices and student activities also depend on safe laboratory travel and hazard-free operation. For example, one of the first environmental impacts of the computer-based learning was the number of electrical cords needed to interface and supply power to the workstations, contributing clutter to many instructional areas.

Technological laboratories also will require a provision of security that will ensure against theft and tampering by students and outside parties. Open space learning environments, while amenable to many learning and teaching methods, pose problems for security, especially in these heavily equipped regions of the laboratory.

Many other investigators have examined the philosophical base for laboratory environments. Todd (Cummings, Jensen, & Todd, 1987) summarized the criteria for environmental design into three areas: flexible, responsive, and economical. Todd's flexibility criteria included adaptability and mobility, while responsive was defined as supportive of learning, both in interdisciplinary efforts and research- and resource-oriented activities. Economical laboratories were characterized as allowing for maximum usage of space, with other factors such as storage space effectively used.

Braybrooke (1986) identified three areas for facility assessment as flexibility, safety, and quality, wherein quality encompassed such factors as lighting, temperature, humidity, physical arrangement, access, and appropriate furniture. Daiber and LaClair (1986) presented an acronym entitled FAM, which stood for flexibility, adaptability, and mobility. "FAM, as one might readily conclude, is not intended to provide specific and exact steps for conducting a facility renovation. It simply provides a very general framework within which some initial study and investigation can be taken" (p. 132).

The theme of flexibility, which encompasses a variety of other terms such as mobility, adaptability, and transformability, has permeated the philosophies of environmental and facility planners. As will be evident in this chapter, this theme will remain prominent.

Laboratories for the Future

Throughout education, changes in the approach to the learning environment has various implications for technology education. Computer-assisted instruction, material learning centers, various learning theories, and new curricular models are a few of the factors having a major impact on what the laboratories of the future should look like. General laboratories and general unit shops served well the philosophies and demands of traditional industrial education courses, but as the discipline has evolved to reflect technology studies, new laboratories that support the inclusive nature of the discipline, must continue to evolve. In many cases, these will be developed from the existing facilities, and will require major adjustments to the traditional laboratories. Curriculum philosophy and content updates must guide the selection of instructional strategies and learning activities. These, in turn, should guide the selection of equipment, resources, tools, materials, furniture, and instructional technologies.

Ramifications of Technology in the Classroom

Throughout history, various technologies and inventions have led to meaningful applications for the teaching and learning environment, especially in the instructional technologies. Some would say that the slateboard and chalk were among the first technological objects in the classroom. In this century, the implications for communication technology may be found in the wide range of media devices, such as projectors, televisions, VCR's, filmstrips, and audio recorders. Educational philosophies and technologies are still changing rapidly; witness the impact of video recorders, compact laser disk technologies, and especially microcomputers. Where would the ramifications of such technological growth be greater but within the area of communication technology and the study of satellites, electronics, graphics, and computers? LaPorte (1987) concluded that from the "predominance of the computer in new technology and the fact that technology is our discipline, we should be the leaders in the use of computers both as the means of instruction and as content to teach" (p. 7). To provide all students with appropriate experiences in communication technology might be the single most important prerequisite to all other phases of education!

Environmental Planning
for Communication Technology

The facility arrangements for technology education courses will vary from school to school, and the activities that will be included will be based on various curricular models, but the communication technology learning environment can be enhanced by the consideration of several factors that are important to most, if not all, programs.

142

Although this chapter will not include the precise facility planning factors, such as recommended equipment and exact size and dimensions of model laboratories, it will discuss and analyze the philosophies and approaches that lead to the final plan of the communication technology laboratory.

Several excellent resources exist for facility planning within the technology education discipline. Although dated by the last decade of advancement into technology education curriculum, Robert D. Brown's Industrial Education Facilities (1979) and the 24th ACIATE Yearbook in this series, *A Guide to Planning Industrial Arts Facilities* (1975), remain beneficial to the current facility planner. The 28th ACIATE Yearbook (1979) also included an historical view of industrial arts laboratory facilities by Gemmill. More recently, the facilities planning committee of the Council on Technology Teacher Education published a monograph entitled, *Planning Technology Teacher Education Learning Environments* (Poulette, 1989). Although directed to higher education programs, it would be a beneficial addition to any facility and environmental planner's collection.

Environmental Planning Versus Facility Planning

Environmental planning must be considered a prerequisite to the planning of the facility. Facility planning includes the determination of equipment and furniture, lighting and color specifications, size of areas, door and window specifications, chalkboard and bulletin board peripherals, and a variety of other aspects that are architecturally specific. On the other hand, environmental planning establishes the philosophical guidelines for facility planning by studying carefully the implications of such things as size, lighting, and furniture. More importantly, environmental planning encompasses the learning theories and instructional theories that are used to facilitate learning, and therefore includes many other considerations that are prerequisite to facility planning. Although many facets of environmental planning are applicable across all educational facilities, there is a good chance that many students will never have been introduced to practical hands-on activities that allow for reinforcement of cognitive knowledge prior to entering technology education courses. For this reason alone, environmental planning for communication technology courses is still new and exploratory, but it demands that old ideas about learning be related to new technologies that comprise the instructional methods, as well as the content of the curriculum.

143

Implications of Classroom Learning Theory

Learning theorists such as Pavlov, Thorndike, Guthrie, Hull, Skinner (Bolles, 1975) have, for years, studied the aspects of why learning happens. Definitions of learning, while diverse, share the common tenet of change. Through time, and across the disciplines of psychology and education, theorists have composed definitions that encompassed various aspects and amounts of "experience," "behavior," "reinforcement," "practice," and "environment." Yoakham and Simpson (Snelbecker, 1934, p. 13) provided a definition that is appropriate to the communication technology learning environment.

> Learning is active. Learning is a function of the total situations surrounding the child. Learning is guided by purpose and consists of living and doing, in having experiences and seeking to understand the meaning of them.

Several questions have been asked within the realm of education regarding why some students learn and others don't. Included are questions regarding the conditions under which students learn best and what arrangement or instructional conditions are most appropriate. Technology education and the study of communication technology provides an excellent opportunity to analyze the implications of many classroom learning theories while planning the appropriate learning environment.

Implications of Instructional Theory

As discussed in the previous section, the manner in which we build the learning environment is affected by the ways that we perceive students to learn. Another factor that demands attention would be the instructional theories that also help determine the educational methods we use. Snelbecker (1985) defined instructional theory as "an integrated set of principles which prescribe guidelines for arranging conditions to achieve educational objectives" (p. 19). The hands-on activities that are the heritage of the technology education discipline reflect the technology teacher's instructional ideology. Through the years, technology education teachers have utilized instructional methods that represent their theories for facilitating and managing instruction. As the discipline continues, the purposes for lectures, demonstrations, and presentations must be constantly reviewed and blended with role-playing, simulations and hands-on activities, as well as other problem solving exercises, in the proper environment, to culminate in a learning experience for the student. An excellent source for additional study is the 37th CTTE Yearbook, *Instructional Strategies for Technology Education* (Kemp & Schwaller, 1988). The formidable task of the communication technology teacher is to blend instructional strategies within the context of the technical facility to complement the learning styles of the students.

The Impact of Computer Technology

Computers have affected the learning environment more than any other technological achievement. The abilities of computers to process information, store masses of information, create visual effects, and simulate the conditions of science and technology are still increasing at phenomenal rates. A number of factors initially prevented the impact of computer technology from being realized to its fullest extent: budgets, resistance to change, lack of available software, and learning theories that did not allow for individualized instruction.

Computers In Communication Technology

Computers have been targeted by some educators as instructional tools that can be used in all phases of the curriculum. Such skills as keyboarding, word processing, programming, and graphic generation have quickly been infused into many courses throughout the public school program. In communication technology studies, computers must be used for processing, storing, and sending information. In addition, a study of the entire realm of computer technology may be made, including the invention and history of computers, the impact of computers on society, the electronic composition of computers, and how to analyze the differences in computer technologies. As technology education continues to address the needs of a technologically literate society, the study and use of computers will be a dominant factor in communication technology.

In addition to computer literacy and computer usage, computer-assisted instruction may be critical in establishing a proper teaching and learning environment. As computers became available within educational programs, especially at the higher education level, ways of having computers provide instruction were developed, leading to the many applications of computer-assisted instruction (CAI).

Futurists predicted classrooms wherein the computer would be the instructor via a monitor, and students could simply ask and answer questions at their terminals. Educational leaders at all levels were searching for room within budgets to buy computers, based solely on the fact that a new technology must be a better technology. However, even as microcomputers lowered hardware costs and increased capacities, and as masses of application software became available, CAI has yet to evolve as a superior means of presenting instruction. In fact, as with most multimedia, it has left much to be desired, yet has found its place with the instructional technologies as another valuable tool.

Computers continue to impact instruction in a variety of ways. As a management device, teachers are able to better organize their materials and utilize grade book programs, allowing more time for instructional preparation. As a word- and graphic-processing device, course materials and handouts are becoming more professional looking and more attractive to the reader. And, as instructional tools, computers, through advanced software programs, have the capabilities of simulating conditions that could not otherwise reach the technology education laboratories. LaPorte (1987) envisioned simulations of laser hardware and electronic circuit design and analysis. As well, he envisioned the use of computers to control machines, motors, and lights; to access national computer data bases for current product information and research; to interact with laser disk videos for touring inaccessible industries; to facilitate desktop publishing as classroom activities; and to establish teleconferencing with other schools. These capabilities are within reach of the current classroom, and should be considered as essential ingredients for providing students with opportunities to see communication technology in action.

Planning Computer Learning Centers

The consideration of a computer learning center is appropriate for all phases of education in our schools today and in the future. A computer learning center, within the scope of technology education, should be planned in such a way as to contain a variety of computers, and perhaps could be used by other disciplines besides technology education; or, depending on the size of the school, solely by the technology education area. In much the same manner that libraries have provided the resources of books and periodicals, the computer technology center can provide a rich education through such resources as CAI software, application programs for the technology education activities, and independent programming opportunities.

As the planning develops for a technology education program and learning environment, the potential of a computer learning center in helping the program meet its goals and purposes merits consideration. It is within the communication technology area that sufficient support is most likely. Creation of technical graphics and other design documentation, communication interfacing, and desktop publishing are all opportunities that utilize the computer so that students can experience the latest technological impacts of the communication area. Computer literacy also provides a basis for experiencing simulations of all areas of technology education. While simulation is not sufficient in itself, the prerequisite experiences can be most valuable and even time-saving. As well, the opportunities provided by national computer data bases and bulletin boards for research and general reading can provide invaluable experiences for students.

While the computer center can provide meaningful experiences, extra effort will be required to maintain the center. Maintenance costs, continuous hardware and software upgrading, integrations of computer activities with other activities, and even physical arrangement for adequate access can encompass the duties of the communication technology faculty. Maintaining security, controlling environmental conditions, and networking feasible arrangements within a flexible learning environment are other challenges for the communication teacher.

Planning For Independent Study and Individualized Instruction

As students progress through the educational system, individual differences are easily identified, and philosophies have emerged to attempt to address these differences through personalized instruction and learning centers in the classroom. Few teachers would intentionally suppress the creative potential of students. Yet, as is often the case, the planning of the learning environment fails to provide the means whereby independent study and individualized instruction can take place. The communication technology laboratory must successfully address the need for activities of an independent nature, such as a research and development project. The needs of students who attain a higher level of achievement, as well as the remediation of those who need to explore further the various topics, must be accompanied by the learning environment.

With little sacrifice of space, a limited general laboratory for communication technology could house an area for independent study through such devices as electric response boards, displays, devices, pocket charts, or multimedia devices such as projection boxes, or VCRs (Morlan, 1974). Smaller school systems could have an independent study area for more than one technology education subject area.

One rewarding aspect of communication technology instruction is that, as part of their learning experiences, capable students can create learning center activities for use by others. Expressing the content of communication technology while using the methods and practices of communication systems is an excellent way for students to develop an appreciation for the discipline, while helping others to experience new technologies in interesting ways.

Environmental Characteristics

The environmental characteristics of a communication technology laboratory may vary according to the grade level, program objectives, and curricular model. A carefully planned environment will complement the goals and purposes of technology education, and will enhance the experiences that students should be expected to have in a communication technology program. As expressed earlier, facility planning must build on knowing and understanding the environment under which learning best takes place.

Characteristics of Space, Light, Color, and Sound

In the learning environment, perceptions of space, light, color, and sound are often subliminal in the effects that they have on learning. Students are often compressed in laboratories and areas that are crowded, ineffectually lighted, and perhaps painted with the standardized school selection. Faulty lighting ballasts may provide a constant level of subliminal noise beyond the machines, devices, and conversations, and be detrimental to learning effectiveness. Although the measurement of the effect of such factors is impossible, the consideration of these factors is important. Interior designers have known for years the influence of color on the moods and temperaments of environmental inhabitants. The designer's studio is not a chance compilation of space, light, and color, but is carefully planned to help the origination of new ideas and creations.

Shape and size of classrooms and laboratories are often affected by architectural ideologies that reflect an open-space or closed-space orientation. While open areas can enhance the creativity level of otherwise structured learning, the security of closed areas can help maintain the organizational effectiveness and concentration level of the teacher and learner. The communication laboratory that utilizes open space design will provide the learner with several activity areas separated only by movable partitions or various furniture arrangements, whereas the closed space plan for a communication laboratory will be characterized by separate rooms for separate activities. Gemmill (1979) characterized the advantages of the open space plan as allowing "students freedom to move about and solve problems, an informal learning process, flexible arrangements, and encouragement of innovation and creativity" (p. 107). Surely this describes the current philosophies and tenets of technology education. Although disadvantages exist, the communication technology laboratory will be enhanced by the open space plan. It does require more attention of the teachers or teaching teams to provide students with the guidance that will prevent a "laissez-faire" attitude, visual and audible interference, and unsafe conditions (Gemmill, p. 108) due to the lack of environmental confinement.

The specific details of the visual and audible factors of the environment are extensive in nature. Most facility planning resources encompass the selections of lighting footcandles, color recommendations, and sound planning techniques. Many of the factors are not unique to the communication technology laboratory. However, the drawing and design area should typically be supplied with more footcandles of light than other areas. Users of computer monitors are often affected by improper lighting and reflection. In addition, consideration for multimedia presentation and creation should be made. Instruction, activity, general safety, and aesthetics are all important factors to consider when planning lighting, both artificial and natural.

While requiring more light for many activities, the communication laboratory area demands less attention to noise control than the other areas of technology education. While not totally void of noise generation, (like several dot-matrix printers generating graphics at the same time), most activities will not be accompanied by the same level of noise generation as manufacturing or construction processes.

Implications of Shapes and Sizes

Over time, school architects have experimented with a variety of classroom and building shapes to help create better learning environments. Octagonal and hexagonal pods have been used to cluster various areas together. Circular classrooms and centered presentation platforms were introduced in attempts to help enhance what would otherwise be a somewhat boring rectangle of rows and columns. Despite attention to irregular classrooms, little evolution has occurred in the development of effective, non-traditional laboratories. Laboratories are often merely calculated carefully per square foot per student to provide the most inexpensive facility available. As environmental planning advances beyond the boundaries of traditional classrooms, the size must necessarily be increased to accommodate the various learning areas that must exist within technology education, especially for instruction of communication technologies and systems.

Area Planning

In the traditional industrial education laboratory, auxiliary areas, such as a library area or a project display area, were often planned into each facility to provide for a variety of activities. As philosophies and curriculum models have advanced to complement instructional strategies and learning theory, the needs and purposes of these areas demand periodic review. Incorporation of creative problem solving and personalized instruction activities, for example, demands an examination of traditional area planning principles. Again, flexibility in the teaching and learning environment is essential to the successful learning experience.

General area planning can begin with conceptual models of the laboratory arrangement. Figure 8.1 illustrates a conceptual model for a limited general laboratory for communication technology.

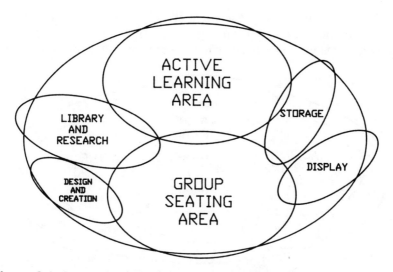

Figure 8.1: Conceptual model – general laboratory.

Figure 8.2 illustrates how this conceptual model might appear as translated into an open space rectangular facility. Additional space would need to be considered for a computer center, a darkroom, or faculty office. As designed, the laboratory provides an environment conducive to multiple activities in an organized manner. In this example, students can move from the group seating to research and study, to idea creation, to the activity area, and similarly to the storage or display areas.

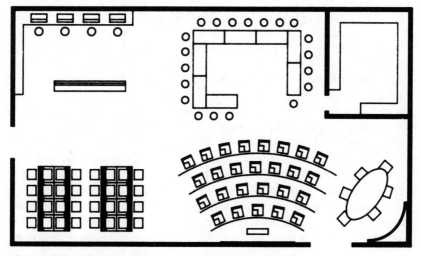

Figure 8.2: Design layout – general laboratory.

Figure 8.3 illustrates a conceptual model that facilitates the sharing of the design and creation area, group seating area, and library and research area with another curriculum area of technology education.

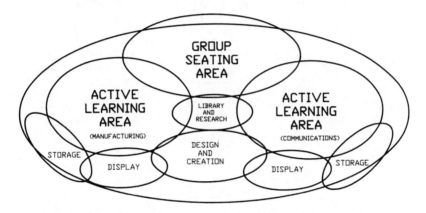

Figure 8.3: Conceptual model – shared laboratory.

In addition to the considerations for flexibility of activity types, the learning environment must be conducive to various group sizes. The success of the program can hinge on the ability of the environment to simultaneously facilitate small group activities, large group activities, individualized independent study, variations in groupings, and even multi-age or multi-course groupings.

The Group Seating Area

Most technology education courses that accommodate groups of students require a certain amount of group organization for presentations. To provide seating for lectures, large class demonstrations, media presentations, and even various housekeeping tasks, a group seating area is desirable. As well, students in an arrangement conducive to graphics layout and design or computer processing will most likely be very poorly arranged for formal presentations. Avoid crowded situations, and provide for the visibility of all students through offset seating arrangements, or U-shaped seating around a large demonstration area. This area must easily provide for presentations by VCR, overhead projectors, computer demonstrations, as well as general lectures. The size of the program often dictates that the group seating area be located so as to be accessible to other technology education areas for split scheduling, multi-group presentations, and student organization meetings.

Demonstration Area

As communication technology instruction is conducted in a variety of ways, the consideration of an area for small "close-up" group demonstration is also important. This could be an area where students can gather around a chalkboard or marker board and either stand or sit in chairs to have a process or product quickly demonstrated. It could also be designed around a computer workstation that is connected to a projector system or is monitored by video camera. The ability to view demonstrations at close range is critical to the successful presentation of many communication technology topics. Various approaches can be taken to the proper demonstration area. The use of folding chairs or tables allows for the clearing of the demonstration area for other purposes. On occasion, the demonstration area could be used as a learning center. For example, if the laboratory only has one oscilloscope, students could take their completed circuit activities to the demonstration area for testing. An instructional program can benefit from the ability to transport the instruction to the student, instead of always transporting the student to the group seating area or to the lone chalkboard at the front of the room. Transportable demonstration units can provide additional potential to the instructional plan for the effective teaching environment in the communication technology laboratory.

Design and Creation Area

Critically important to the teaching and learning of technology education is, and will remain, the activities of design and creation. As students study and learn about communication technology, the reinforcement and application of principles requires the design and creation of drawings, schematics, models, and other experiments, exercises, and activities. The area for this may be merely tables and chairs. As well, the consideration of drawing equipment, whether it be sketching boards or drafting machines, is also appropriate.

Access to computers, either through a main computer learning center or an extension area of the main classroom, will be necessary. If the technology education area supports a computer learning center, the design and creation of graphics that support and supplement activities can be generated with the output devices available. Futurist projections for the communication technology laboratory include the possibility of "textbooks" on compact disk, activity plans on floppy disk, and student feedback constantly accessible through a local data base. As technology becomes more affordable, the communication technology area of technology education could very well support the computer learning center for design and creation facets of all other areas of the technology education program.

Active Learning Area

In addition to the design and creation of ideas and activities, the communication technology laboratory will be the scene of several instructor-developed or externally provided activities, experiments, and exercises. Therefore, the active learning area is probably the most crucial area to be developed, for the ideas and attitudes must be developed and reinforced by the activity that provides the learning experience for the student. The work may take the form of an electronic model, a graphic layout, or a balsa wood model. The tools involved may be so diverse as to include razor knives, drawing triangles, and multimeters. The active learning area should be able to accommodate the entire class of students at one time, even though on many occasions several students will be conducting other activities in other areas, for example, the library and research area.

As alluded to earlier, learning centers for independent study may be appropriate for the active learning area. Again, flexibility and safety are key ingredients for enhanced experiences. The provision for students to work in a variety of group sizes, on a variety of different activities, while being supervised in a safe environment, is demanded by the technology curriculum today.

Library and Research Area

Even within industry, an area that provides resources for the study of technology is essential. Students and teachers must also have access to periodicals, books, software, instructional aids, and other devices. Although much of this can be handled through the school's library system, the rewards of having immediate availability to necessary references are desirable. This area will require a certain amount of shelf or filing space, some tabletop area, and should accommodate a small proportion of the enrollment at any time. This area could also be the primary location of learning center activities and displays. Of primary importance is that students feel the library research area is accessible to them without alienating them from the action of other students involved in activities and exercises. For students to benefit from the research and library area, they should sense that it provides them with information regarding the latest technological trends, rather than just existing as a museum of artifacts from previous decades of technological growth.

Machine Area

Depending on the size and content of the particular communication technology curriculum, the laboratory may also be the scene for large pieces of equipment that demand isolation or safety boundaries. Offset presses, photography equipment, and various other media equipment may need to be strategically located in a machine area for close supervision and student control.

Display Area

The display area may serve several objectives, including, but not limited to, the promotion of the technology education program to others, a place to exhibit student work, and a place to provide information to the students about the related topics. A well designed environment draws the attention of visitors to the program in addition to the students who spend time in the laboratory daily. There are always a variety of motivational posters, informational guidesheets, advertisements, and journal articles available that would enhance the learning environment, especially if placed strategically for viewing and studying while within the communication technology laboratory.

The nature of communication technology activities will often be oriented to require larger amounts of wall space for display. While computer and electronic models and experiences are conducive to tabletop presentation, graphic communications are more amenable to being wall-mounted, perhaps on bulletin boards. Teachers who fail to take advantage of the display area of the laboratory or facility are eliminating the strength of the reinforcement that is so essential to culminating the learning experience, even as it is being used to introduce others to the world of communication technology for the first time.

Storage Areas and Rooms

The variety of exercises and activities that have been and will be developed for assisting instruction in communication technology require an organized and extended storage area, or perhaps a storage room. As students become involved in experiments, activities, and other projects too cumbersome for mobility around the school, student storage space becomes essential. As different topics are covered throughout the course of events, various items and equipment pieces will need to be stored as well. The well planned learning environment will allow for the quick and organized storage of instructional equipment, student tools and equipment, supplies, and student projects and devices.

Again, as technologies change, and as curricula continue to reflect current technology, it becomes apparent that the future learning tools and activities cannot be predicted. It is beyond the scope of this chapter to recommend storage specifics. As with much in the current learning environment, shelving, lockers, and cabinet arrangements must be mobile, adaptable, and transformable, while still providing the instructor and student with a reasonable amount of organization and security.

Considerations for Classroom Arrangements

Although an ideal classroom may not be possible due to crowded conditions, poor planning, old facilities, or minimal budgets, every program can strive for the flexibility it takes to allow students the variety of experiences and opportunities essential to a good education. All students need to experience activities in several of the mini-environments that were expressed by the areas explained earlier. Of the aforementioned areas, students should not expect to spend an inappropriate amount of time in lecture/presentation, design and creation, or library research. In the event that some arrangements don't allow for certain areas, classroom arrangements should be considered that allow for as many different experiences as possible. Under crowded conditions, efforts should be made to search out other areas of the school facility, such as the library for learning centers, or closets and storerooms for storage areas outside the technology education area.

The physical arrangement of tables and drafting or computer workstations can conform to a variety of layouts. The instructor desk located in front of tables or workstations that all face one direction provides easier visual concentration for both student and teacher, but does not accommodate electrical wiring access or travel access to all students.

Facing rows of workstations toward each other in back-to-back rows can economize space and better facilitate supervision, but faces half the students away from the other half. The instruction can take place at one end of the rows with all students facing sideways to the workstations.

A third option is to arrange tables around walls in an L-shape, U-shape, or complete perimeter O-shape, which allows for central supervision by the teacher, but is less conducive to demonstration from a particular focal point.

While less amenable to traffic and electrical access, workstations can be arranged in pods or cells of four tables each, wherein each of the four workstations faces another. While allowing some group privacy for students, individual students can be distracted by the visual contact with others in the cell.

Facility planning often provides the classroom arrangement the opportunity for change to and from different table arrangements, even as the school year progresses. Floor- and ceiling-mounted electrical outlets and networking structures inhibit this freedom to change periodically the structure of the classroom.

The Integration of Equipment and Materials with Instructional Methods and the Learning Environment

The purpose of integrating equipment and materials with instructional methods and technologies is to enhance the learning environment for the students. Too often, teachers assume that students have learned because a presentation has taken place. The effectiveness of the teaching process is affected by various factors, and can often be attributed solely to the ability of the teacher to communicate with the students. The integration of equipment and materials with the instructional methods within the learning environment is a critical task for the teacher. The very essence of teaching is communication, and the lack of the materials and equipment can create problems, but to integrate the equipment and materials so poorly as to suppress communication can be very detrimental to the student experiences. On one hand, the successful teacher must select and work with a variety of devices for instructional purposes, and on the other hand, must select and work with equipment and materials that are pertinent to the area of communication technology. As technologies provide and enhance new types of equipment -- laser disks, video cassette players, facsimile devices, computer projectors -- decisions regarding how these are to be utilized to enhance instruction and decisions regarding how these items fit into the communication technology curriculum must be made.

In summary, it is important to note that new technology does not always guarantee the enhancement of the teacher's ability to provide effective instruction. Hershfield (1981) pointed out that:

> . . . if we looked in on the average American classroom today, we would find one teacher or professor standing in front of a group of students, presenting material. At the elementary and secondary school levels, we might also find the teacher posing questions, and accepting responses from students with up-raised hands. Thus, the education process in the average classroom has changed little since before the invention of movable type in 1448. (p. 3)

The communication technology teacher must remember to communicate to the student, and hopefully the effective use of technology can enhance this endeavor.

Equipment Selection to Complement Activities

Equipment selection and purchase is one of the most important decisions that teachers and administrators make regarding the expenditure of institutional funds. Careful analysis of how the equipment will complement activities is often overlooked. As well, equipment is becoming technologically obsolete at such a rapid pace that educators often become frustrated with the level of technology that is affordable. For example, the Apple II computer may be antiquated compared to the IBM PC-XT, which may be less powerful than the Macintosh II, which will surely seem antiquated in a few years. Decisions are also necessary regarding the choices between "industrial-strength" machines, "tabletop" machines that perform similar functions, or even computer programs that merely simulate the various processes. The level of instruction and the availability of resources and local industrial support may play an important role in the types of equipment that particular laboratories house. An important factor to remember, however, is that equipment does not constitute the curriculum. If used properly, equipment enhances the learning experience.

Equipment for a communication laboratory will provide for learning experiences with graphic production systems, technical design systems, data or electronic communication systems, optic systems, and audio and video communication systems. Helsel and Jones (1986) categorized areas of communications as electronic and graphic, which helped identify types of equipment, subjects, and content that must be addressed in the learning environment. As outlined, the earlier levels of communications technology might address photography, offset printing, screen process printing, drafting, radio broadcast, video tape, and computers. More advanced studies in photography, printing, drafting, and further studies in radio, television, computer graphics, and word processing would likely be a part of the next level of study.

The key to providing a successful learning environment is to always return to the goals and objectives of the curriculum and the discipline philosophy. For many years, industrial education was tools-oriented and project-driven. Today, communication technology studies demand that equipment and tools enhance or complement activities that reinforce the study of technology, rather than determine the projects and exercises that are given to students.

Technology Lag and "Available" Technology

In addition to the lag in technology within the educational setting, textbooks, school suppliers, and especially classroom teachers, often lag behind in their level of knowledge pertinent to the current technology. Instructors who do not want to settle for the "available" technology of their particular program can easily become frustrated. As microcomputers continue to increase in processing speed and memory capacity, and as software companies introduce new and more powerful versions of programs periodically, the learning environment must not suffer. The effective program will work with the available technology to present and teach the aspects of communication technology that are pertinent to the student, with the realistic understanding that lag will always exist as technology continues to double every few years.

The goals and objectives of the communication technology program can be met in an environment that deals with technology lag through a positive approach and encourages the students to go beyond the classroom with their own research and development. The challenge facing the communication technology teacher is great. The information revolution that has become identified with the 1980's has been centered around the computers and electronic wizardry. Students will be motivated if they sense that their studies will be essential to their future existence, rather than about the past. For this reason alone, the research and experiment aspect of the teaching and learning environment must be critically examined to ensure that students can fill in the gap created by the technological advances not reflected in the laboratory setting.

Instructional Technologies

Instructional technologies are currently being developed that will continue to have an impact on the way teachers teach and the way students learn. As alluded to earlier, there is nothing inherent about technological devices that causes learning to be enhanced or the process of learning to quicken. Television and radio, films and filmstrips, records and tapes, and typewriters and drafting machines have had minimal impact upon the nature of the curriculum and the quality of formal school education (Hershfield, 1981). However, through such technologies as interactive videos, massive electronic data bases, fiber optic communications, and artificial intelligence software, attempts to enhance delivery systems for the presentation of all subjects will continue. The area of communication technology in the technology education curriculum must reach out and grasp these technologies, incorporate them into the instructional scheme as applicable, and most importantly, include them in the course content.

As instructional technologies change, the realm of education must still be the system that serves to facilitate for the change in the lives of students. The determination of curriculum, the planning and implementation of curriculum, and the review and analysis of the entire system must continually work in cooperation with the instructional technologies, the computers, the media devices, and, of course, the student and the parent, if change is to happen.

The Need for Creative Problem Solving in the Teaching and Learning Environment

The importance of creative problem solving in the teaching and learning environment cannot be overstated. As students are educated in mass quantities, the creative urge is easily suppressed through rote memorization, group exercises, and an overemphasis on intellectual skills. The total development of individuals must include a concentrated effort to develop the creative problem-solving capabilities. The communication technology environment must provide a variety of "thinking" experiences. It is rather presumptuous to believe that the typical learning environments of years past will suffice for many of the problem-solving activities that are characteristic of the communication technology environment. Role playing and simulation of solving technological problems, even if it is an egg-drop protection device, is exciting and motivating if given the proper setting and preparation. Many facets of education are uninteresting because students don't feel capable, or don't feel like the goal is worth the time and effort, or, perhaps, the activities don't satisfy the desires the students have for being involved. The creative problem solving activity must not only be rewarding, appropriate, and desirable, it must be an activity the student feels he/she can be successful with.

Although the underlying themes of creative problem solving have emerged with the general curriculum at all age levels, with such things as word puzzles and drawing games, most students are exposed to more and more rigidity and structure as the curriculum matures. Communication technology deals with more than an industry that has only one answer to any problem. There are often seemingly impossible challenges that continually call upon the problem-solving skills of all individuals. Within the secondary schools, objectives for developing life-long learning skills and conceptual learning techniques must replace ideologies of skill-specific training on a few tools and industrial processes. Ideas and creativity are the resources by which new creations and inventions will be developed. It is with the realization that our future technologists, engineers, and scientists are, at this time, within our school systems that we should approach the challenge of education with a creative problem solving emphasis.

Summary

This chapter has dealt with the planning of the educational environment that must exist within the laboratory that focuses on the learning of communication technologies. There can be no doubt that the learning environment for a dynamic discipline such as communication technology must be:

*flexible
*friendly
*motivating
*adventurous
*scholarly
*unique
*challenging
*beneficial
*physically safe
*psychologically secure
*accessible and amenable to all students -- the gifted,
  learning disabled, and handicapped

As well, the learning environment must also be the scene of:

*learner success
*relevant and practical activities
*positive reinforcement
*constructive feedback
*active participation
*practice opportunities
*interdisciplinary study
*problem solving
*problem finding
*simulation
*role playing
*research and development

Finally, the student must be actively involved in developing skills in the following areas:

*reasoning ability
*life-long learning abilities
*self discovery and independence
*enthusiasm for learning
*appreciation for technology
*inquiry, observation, and exploration
*inventiveness
*intuition
*conceptualization
*career and education decision-making
*all domains of learning
*intellectual courage
*communications

References

Bolles, R. C. (1975). *Learning theory*. New York: Rinehart and Winston.

Brown, R. D. (1979). *Industrial education facilities: A handbook for organization and management*. Boston, MA: Allyn and Bacon, Inc.

Cummings, P. L., Jensen, M., & Todd, R. (1987). Facilities for technology education. *The Technology Teacher, 46*(7), 7-10.

Gemmill, P. R. (1989). From unit shop to laboratory of technologies. *The Technology Teacher.* (special commemorative 50th anniversary edition), 1-10.

Gemmill, P. R. (1979). Industrial arts laboratory facilities: Past, present, and future. *Industrial arts education: Retrospect, prospect*, 28th Yearbook, American Council on Industrial Arts Teacher Education, pp. 86-111.

Helsel, L. D., & Jones, R. E. (1986). Undergraduate technology education: The technical sequence. *Implementing technology education*, 35th Yearbook, American Council on Industrial Arts teacher education, pp. 171-200.

Hershfield, A. E. (1981, January). Developing technology to enhance the educational process. In *Technology and education*, (pp. 1-15), Proceedings of the National Conference of Technology and Education, Washington, D.C.

Kemp, W. H., & Schwaller, A. E. (Eds.). (1988). *Instructional strategies for technology education*, 37th Yearbook, Council on Technology Teacher Education.

LaPorte, J. E. (1987). A vision of computers in technology education. *The Technology Teacher, 46*(8), 5-7.

Moon, D. E. (Ed.). (1975). Introduction. *A guide to the planning of industrial arts facilities*, 24th Yearbook, American Council on Industrial Arts Teacher Education.

Morlan, J. E. (1974). *Classroom learning centers.* Belmont,CA: Lear Siegler, Inc./Fearon Publishers.

Poulette, E. (Ed.). (1989). *Planning technology teacher education learning environments.* Reston, VA: Council on Technology Teacher Education.

Snelbecker, G. E. (1985). *Learning theory, instructional theory, and psycho-educational design.* Lanham, MD: University Press of America, Inc.

Chapter 9

EVALUATING AND IMPROVING THE COMMUNICATION TEACHING AND LEARNING PROCESS

William E. Dugger, Jr.
Professor
Technology Education Program Area
Virginia Polytechnic Institute and State University
Blacksburg, Virginia

Introduction

A detailed review of literature in the industrial arts and technology education profession indicated that some research and evaluation on the teaching and learning process has taken place over the past thirty years. This has been primarily a result of the efforts of the Council on Technology Teacher Education (CTTE, formerly the ACIATE), graduate student research, and professionals doing in-depth demographic research. Evaluation can be added under the banner of research with much accomplished over the past three decades. It has only been recently that research has been attempted in the curriculum organizers such as communication.

One of the earliest documents on research was the 9th Yearbook of the American Council of Industrial Arts Teacher Education (ACIATE, 1960), *Research in Industrial Arts Education*. The content of the book centered around significant research in industrial arts teacher education as well as scientific procedures and theoretical orientation research in industrial arts education. Another section in this yearbook dealt with needed research in industrial arts teacher education and the classroom.

The second major research effort in the 1960's was undertaken in 1962 and 1963 by Marshall L. Schmitt, Specialist for Industrial Arts, and Albert L. Pelley, Research Assistant for Industrial Arts, of the U. S. Department of Health, Education, and Welfare. Their significant research was titled *Industrial Arts Education: A Survey of Programs,*

Teachers, Students, and Curriculum. This research was published in 1966 and provided for the first time a comprehensive review of the industrial arts programs in the public schools in the United States. Before this research, little factual information was available for curriculum specialists to use for the improvement of industrial arts education.

One of the unique features of the Schmitt-Pelley study was that several factors which influenced educational programs were examined, such as teachers' backgrounds, abilities of students, teaching problems, methods of teaching, course offerings, and instructional content. These data were reported in relation to the enrollment size and type of school. The study also revealed areas where improvements were needed in industrial arts education.

The Schmitt-Pelley study surveyed both principals and classroom teachers in schools nationwide. In 1962-63, 2,259 principals and 3,040 teachers were randomly selected to respond to the two instruments. Of the sample taken, 95.1 percent of the principals responded and 93.7 percent of the teachers returned their forms for analysis. The report provided the first analysis of industrial arts programs nationwide. It was a most important benchmark study in that it provided us with some understanding of who we were and what we were doing in the public school environment. Also, it was important in that it provided the original basis for some longevity studies in the future.

The 13th ACIATE Yearbook was devoted to *Classroom Research in Industrial Arts* (1964). It discussed such topics as the research process, tools for classroom research, interpreting and evaluating research, and selected problem areas with implication for research in industrial arts.

In 1966 the ACIATE published its 15th Yearbook dealing with the *Status of Research in Industrial Arts.* This was the third effort by this council to look at research within the profession. Some of the topics covered in the 15th Yearbook were: research related to the achievement of industrial arts objectives, research and experimentation as a teaching method in industrial arts, research related to industrial arts teacher education, staff studies and other non-degree research in industrial arts, and finally, securing funds for research in industrial arts teacher education. At its time of publication, this yearbook provided valuable information on what was happening in our field.

From the mid-1960's through the early 1970's, most of the research in industrial arts education was developmental research on curriculum. Throughout this important time period in our history, many curriculum projects were underway, resulting in a number of curriculum approaches being developed, field tested, implemented, and evaluated nationwide. There is little evaluative research on effects of these curriculum efforts in our profession.

In 1978, the U. S. Department of Education funded the *Standards for Industrial Arts Programs Project* at Virginia Polytechnic Institute and State University. One of the major components of this effort was to develop a national data base for industrial arts. In 1980, as a result of surveying over 2,200 schools nationwide, Virginia Polytechnic Institute and State University published a *Report of Survey Data for Industrial Arts Education* (1981) which gave the collective views of principals, guidance counselors, industrial arts department chairpersons, and state supervisors, on school programs at this point in time.

This provided an important second national benchmark for the profession's use in analyzing strengths/weaknesses. Some comparisons were drawn between the results of the standards data base study and the Schmitt-Pelley study some fifteen years earlier. Also, there were quite a few new questions dealing with the profession at that time. The area of communication was identified as an emerging subject matter area listed in the standards data base. This was a result of the profession adding the clusters of communication, manufacturing, construction, and transportation to their portfolio of subject matter areas.

In 1981, this project published the *Standards for Industrial Arts Programs*. Included in this document was a mandate for school programs to include such curriculum clusters as communication, manufacturing, construction, and transportation. Four years later, in 1985, the *Standards for Technology Education* were developed, which added further emphasis to a need to move away from industrial classifiers to purely technological curriculum organizers within the profession. Again, communication surfaced as an important curriculum area listed in the *Standards for Technology Education*.

In the 1980's, there began a series of longitudinal studies dealing with the profession. In each January issue of the *Industrial Education magazine, Rex Miller has provided an annual review of the job openings and teacher vacancies with the profession. Since 1985, School Shop* and the International Technology Education Association have supported the annual survey of the profession which has been published in *School Shop* and *The Technology Teacher* magazines. This research has been conducted at Virginia Polytechnic Institute and State University by Dugger, Fowler, Jones, and Starkweather

(1985-1989). This provides a listing of a number of areas of interest in research in industrial arts/technology education. Also sponsored by these two groups is the annual survey of the state supervisors of technology education. This has been published in separate issues of School Shop and *The Technology Teacher*. It provides a perspective on the opinions of state and territorial supervisors of our profession.

It is through such efforts as these that we have a better understanding of what is happening in our profession. Most of the research has been generic and has not been specific to subject matter or cluster curriculum areas within the profession such as communication.

The Process Of Evaluation

Education evaluation is a process whereby the worth or value of an education process or product is determined for the purpose of making decisions. Often, research and evaluation are mistaken for each other. Research and evaluation differ very much in purpose, although they may use the same methods and techniques. This was aptly documented by Worthen and Sanders in their book *Educational Evaluation, Alternative Approaches and Practical Guidelines* (1987) when they stated, "Research and evaluation are no more synonymous, just because they employ common approaches, tools, and techniques, than performing surgery is synonymous with doing an autopsy" (1987, p. 28).

Numerous writers have classified research (Borg & Gall, 1983; Kerlinger, 1975) and various types of evaluation (Worthen & Sanders, 1987; Stufflebeam & Webster, 1980; Worthen, 1984). Probably one of the best definitions of basic research and applied research (often believed to be synonymous with evaluation) was written four decades ago by the National Science Foundation, and it stated that:

> Basic research is directed toward increase of knowledge; it
> is research where the primary aim of the investigator is a
> fuller understanding of the subject under study rather than
> a practical application thereof. Applied research is directed
> toward practical applications of knowledge. (1960, p. 5)

Worthen and Sanders (1987) probably have done as good a job as any of the educational writers in differentiating between research and evaluation, which are generally undertaken for different reasons. See Figure 9.1 for a listing of differences between research and evaluation.

Research	Evaluation
1. Satisfies curiosity by advancing knowledge	1. Contributes to the solution of practical problems through judging the value of whatever is evaluated
2. Seeks conclusions	
3. Involves "law-giving" (nomothetic) activities	2. Leads to discussions
4. Many times the researcher sets his/her own tasks	3. Involves description of particular (idiographic) activities or things
5. Attempts to generate new or scientific knowledge	4. Undertaken at the request of a client
6. Generalizable across time	
7. Judged by the criteria of internal and external validity	5. Attempts to assess the value of an activity or thing
8. Sets its own time schedule (barring economic constraints)	6. Generalizable for usually only short periods of time
	7. Judged by the criteria of accuracy, credibility, usability, feasibility, and propriety
	8. Time bound . . . adhering to

Figure 9.1: Differences between research and evaluation (excerpted from Worthen and Sanders, 1987, 29-34).

In 1967, Michael Scriven stated that there were two basic types of evaluation: formative and summative. These distinctions of the types of evaluation have become widely accepted within the educational community. Formative evaluation is sometimes referred to as "process" evaluation, since it is conducted during the operation of a program to provide evaluative information which is useful in improving the program while it is ongoing. Summative evaluation is sometimes called "product" evaluation, and it is completed at the finish of a program. It provides information about the program's worth or merit for those who were involved, or for potential consumers of the program in the future. The role of the two audiences is quite different in formative and summative evaluation. Both types of evaluation are needed in the total evaluation process of a program or instructional method.

A chart showing the differences between formative and summative evaluation appears as Figure 9.2 (Worthen & Sanders, 1987, p. 36).

	Formative Evaluation	Summative Evaluation
Purpose	To improve program	To certify program utility
Audience	Program administrators and staff	Potential consumer or funding agency
Who Should Do It	Internal evaluator	External evaluator
Major Characteristic	Timely	Convincing
Measures	Often informal	Valid/reliable
Frequency of Data Collection	Frequent	Limited
Sample Size	Often small	Usually large
Questions Asked	What is working? What needs to be improved? How can it be improved?	What results occur? With whom? Under what condition? With what training? At what cost?
Design Constraints	What information is needed? When?	What claims do you wish to make?

Figure 9.2: Differences between formative and summative evaluation (excerpted from Worthen and Sanders, 1987, p. 36).

In technology education, most of our efforts would fall under the National Science Foundation's category of evaluation rather than pure research.

Characteristics of Quality Communication Programs

According to Gephart, Ingle, and Carroll, the ultimate goal for evaluating any educational program is the "improvement of student intellectual, social, and maturational development" (1979, p. 88). If there was not a concern for this, all efforts for evaluation would be fruitless.

Quality programs in communication are based on numerous components. Central in determining the value of a communication program is deliberate planning for evaluation in the overall scheme of education. Good communication programs, "just don't happen" . . . they must be carefully planned, conducted, and assessed.

An excellent model developed by Dale L. Bolton (1979) which presents three stages of evaluation is shown in Figure 9.3.

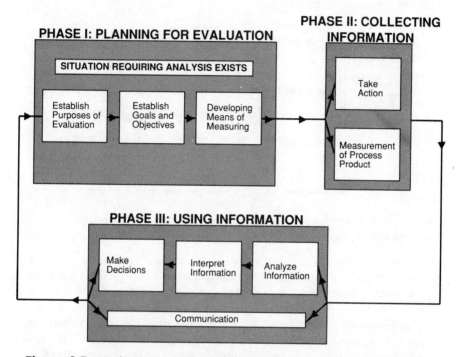

Figure 9.3: *Bolton, D. (1979). The basis for evaluating teaching: Philosophy, context, and purpose. *Planning for the Evaluation of Teaching*, p. 43. Bloomington, IN: Phi Delta Kappa.

Note that Phase I deals with the planning process for evaluation which includes the establishment of purposes, goals, and objectives for the program. Next in this phase is the development of the means of measurement to be utilized. In Phase II, the data is collected. Action is taking place in this process, and measurement of both the processes used in the educational environment as well as the product (the educated youth) is important. During Phase III, the evaluation information is analyzed and interpreted to make decisions. The results of this evaluation are communicated to the responsible parties. Lastly, the results are fed back to the next planning program effort (New Phase I) to begin again this process (Bolton, 1979, p. 43).

Taking this process even further, a systems model was developed in Virginia for technology education and is presented in Figure 9.4 (Virginia Technology Education Service, 1988, p. 8). Technology education is defined as: "the school discipline for the study of the application of knowledge, creativity, and resources to solve problems and extend human potential."

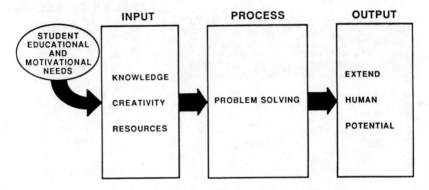

Figure 9.4: A model for technology education (Technology Education Service, Virginia Dept. of Education, 1988, 8).

With the Virginia model as a reference, an evaluation systems model can be developed for communication technology. This model is presented in Figure 9.5. Note that the pupils' educational and motivational needs are the predominant factors in the evaluation model for communication technology. These are sometimes called pre-inputs or "sets" for the evaluation model. The communication inputs are the typical inputs to any classical model, such as the communication tools, communication materials, information about communication processes, energy, capital, and people. These inputs will be fed in the communication processes which are used in any classical communication systems model. First is the process of encoding or modifying information/data into a desired format or pattern for a specific method of transmission or storage.

The second communication process is transmitting. This is the technical process of conveying information from one location to another. Usually the transmission takes place through a channel which could be either by: electromagnetic waves, through fiber optics, through cable, by laser, and from the printed image on the page communicated by light, or many other possible means.

The next communication process is that of receiving, which is the recognition and accepting of information which has been transmitted. Naturally, the receiver must be tuned or connected to the transmitter in order for maximum communication to take place.

Another important communication process is that of storing and/or filing information for use at a later date. This is connected with removing information in the technical process of recalling information from a stored condition, which is designated as retrieving.

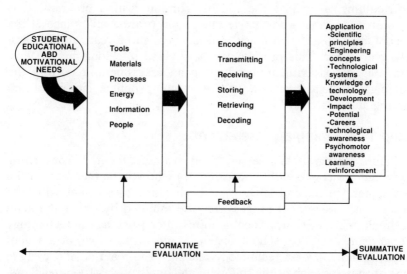

Figure 9.5: Evaluation model for communication technology.

Fifth, the information communicated must be converted or modified into an acceptable format for use. This communication process is often referred to as decoding.

Sixth and lastly, the transfer of information from the information destination back to the source is a feedback process. All of these important communication processes make up the central part of a communication systems model. The desired student outcomes in a communication process involve understanding the successful application of scientific principles, engineering concepts, and technological systems. Also, another desired student outcome is the cognitively acquired knowledge of technology, its development, impact, potential, and careers available to each pupil. Another is technological awareness and capability, as is the use of communication as a learning reinforcement for other subject matters in the school.

The ongoing evaluation of this model can be related back to the two generally acceptable areas of evaluation. The ongoing process of assessing the quality of the inputs, processes, and outputs of any communication process is formative evaluation. This is regular and should take place informally on a daily, weekly, monthly, and yearly basis. There may be actual annual evaluations (summative) done by the school system on the total model.

The Standards for Technology Education may be used as a means for assessing the overall quality of a school's technology education curriculum, as well as the specific communication program. It is recommended that a formative evaluation process take place at the school level on a regular basis at least every three years and preferably every year. This process can be divided into four major steps: planning an assessment, conducting an assessment, reporting the findings of an assessment, and overcoming deficiencies identified during an assessment.

Step 1 - Planning an Assessment

Before a program is assessed, decisions must be made concerning (a) which processes will be assessed, (b) who will be members of the assessment team, and (c) how and when the assessment will take place. The assessment process may be initiated by either the state technology supervisor, a local administrator (such as the technology supervisor for a local school system, a school principal, or a school superintendent), or a technology teacher. The team should include one or more of each of the following: technology classroom teachers, school administrators, students, parents, business and industry representatives, and other consultants. This team should meet and become familiar with the standards and the assessment process.

Step 2 - Conducting the Assessment

The assessment process involves comparing a given technology education program to standards. In the process, the assessment team records whether the program meets, exceeds, or fails to meet each standard.

Step 3 - Reporting the Findings of an Assessment

The assessment team report should identify strengths and weaknesses of the program being assessed. The weaknesses are itemized and explained and suggested priorities for correcting deficiencies are made.

Step 4 - Overcoming Deficiencies Identified During an Assessment

Procedures and resources are employed to overcome deficiencies. The assessment team monitors these procedures to determine their success in correcting deficiencies and recommends a time line for program reassessment.

The summative evaluation process may be used on a limited basis to certify a program's utility. This may be done by an external evaluator, and the results may be used for major program improvement or for public relations purposes. The results of the communication part of a technology education program are usually evaluated, and the school or school system should use the findings for major decision making purposes. Probably accreditation visits by regional and/or state accreditation teams would be considered as summative evaluation. An excellent example of this is the material used by the six regional accrediting associations titled *Evaluative Criteria*, Sixth Edition (1987) and published by the National Study of School Evaluation. This material is used in approximately 95 percent of the schools nationwide for regional accrediting purposes. In this publication, there is a section dealing with description of offerings (subsection IV). In this, Descriptive Criteria #3 states that "instructional content should be drawn from one or more of the areas of communication, construction, manufacturing, and transportation." This is important in that the subject matter is specified in technology education according to the broad clusters and communication is included in this grouping.

Summary

The communication program should be evaluated on a regular and systematic basis. Within this chapter, a review has been presented on the history of evaluation in industrial arts and technology education. Also, the process of evaluation has been discussed in detail, and an evaluation model has been presented for communication technology. It is through evaluation techniques that programs are assessed, and hopefully, as a result of this process, the overall quality of communication technology programs will improve in the future.

References

Bolton, D. L. (1979). The basis for evaluating teaching: Philosophy, context, and purpose. *Planning for the Evaluation of Teaching,* p. 43. Bloomington, IN: Phi Delta Kappa.

Borg, W. R., & Gall, M. D. (1983). *Educational research: An introduction* (4th ed.). New York: Longman.

Dugger, W. E., Bame, E. A., & Pinder, C. A. (1981). *Standards for industrial arts programs.* Blacksburg, VA: Virginia Polytechnic Institute & State University.

Dugger, W. E., Bame, E. A., Pinder, C. A. (1985). *Standards for technology education programs.* Reston, VA: International Technology Education Association.

Dugger, W. E., Fowler, F. S., Jones, A. H., & Starkweather, K. N. (1989). State supervisors report on TE & T & I programs. *School Shop, 48*(10), pp. 23-26.

Dugger, W. E., Fowler, F. S., Jones, A. H., & Starkweather, K. N. (1989). State supervisors report on technology education. *The Technology Teacher, 48*(8), pp. 5-8.

Gephart, W. J., Ingle, R. B., & Carroll, M. R. (1979). Wrap-up: The basis for evaluating teaching. *Planning for the Evaluation of Teaching,* p. 84. Bloomington, IN: Phi Delta Kappa.

Kerlinger, F. N. (1975). *Foundations of behavioral research: Educational, psychological, and sociological inquiry* (2nd ed.). New York: Holt, Rinehart, & Winston.

Miller, R. (1989). IA teachers: Supply and demand. *Industrial Education, 78*(1), pp. 8-13.

National Science Foundation. (1960). *Reviews of data on research and development*(No. 17, NSF-60-10). Washington, DC: Author. National Study of School Evaluation. (1987). *Evaluative criteria,* sixth edition. Falls Church, VA: Author.

Porter, C. B. (Ed.). (1964). *Classroom research in industrial arts,* 13th Yearbook, American Council on Industrial Arts Teacher Education.

Rowlett, J. D. (1966). *Status of research in industrial arts,* 15th Yearbook, American Council on Industrial Arts Teacher Education.

Schmitt, M. L., & Pelley, A. L. (1966). *Industrial arts education, a survey or programs, teachers, students, and curriculum.* Washington, DC: U. S. Government Printing Office.

Scriven, M. (1967). The methodology of evaluation. In R. E. Stake (Ed.), *Curriculum evaluation.* American Educational Research Association Monograph Series on Evaluation, No. 1. Chicago, IL: Rand McNally.

Stufflebeam, D. L., & Webster, W. J. (1980). An analysis of alternative approaches to evaluation. *Educational Evaluation and Policy Analysis, 2*(3), pp. 5-19.

Technology Education Service. (1989). *The technology education curriculum, K-12.* Richmond, VA: Virginia Department of Education.

Van Tassell, R. (Ed.). (1960). *Instructional strategies for technology education,* 9th Yearbook, American Council on Industrial Arts Teacher Education.

Worthen, B. R. (1984). Program evaluation. In *International encyclopedia of education: Research and studies*. Oxford, England: Pergamon Press, Ltd.

Worthen, B. R., & Sanders, J. R. (1973). *Education evaluation: Theory and practice*. Belmont, CA: Wadsworth.

Worthen, B. R., & Sanders, J. P. (1987). *Educational evaluation, alternative approaches and practical guidelines*. White Plains, NY: Longmans.

Chapter 10

A SYNTHESIS OF COMMUNICATION SYSTEMS AND APPROACHES FOR TECHNOLOGY EDUCATION

Jane A. Liedtke
Associate Professor
Department of Industrial Technology
Illinois State University
Normal, Illinois

Introduction

What can children growing up in today's information society expect of tomorrow's world? Isaac Asimov (1989) contended that "we will have a world of the technochild" (p. 56). As educators we will be managing the education of children who have: A. been born with a remote control in their hands, B. seen their parents microwave dinner within 30 seconds, and C. learned to point and click before learning to ride a bicycle (*Personal Computing*, 1988). According to Asimov:

> In the past, three fundamental advances in human communication evolved that altered every facet of our world enormously and permanently. The first advance was speech, the second writing, and the third printing. Now we face a fourth advance in communication every bit as important as the first three - the computer. The fourth revolution will enable most human beings to be more creative than they've ever been before. (p. 56)

What Asimov explained comes as no surprise to the technology educator who has experienced the change from an industrial based society and curriculum to the information age filled with dynamic technological innovations. Asimov's perspective that the computer will impact communication as significantly as printing did is surely accurate. It is perhaps an underestimate of a device which has not fully realized its potential in the home, education, business, industry and government plus the impacts which computers will have on a global society.

178

Major changes in communication as a result of computerization will impact how children and adults are educated and trained. The transition of the processes and products of business and industry will change how people work and the role that work will play in people's lives. People will experience more leisure and/or entertainment time and will be afforded the freedom to participate in a global neighborhood. The ability to have the barriers of language itself solved via software programs will enable people to converse and share information. Easy access to other cultures or connecting to relatives or colleagues in foreign countries will create a new world view.

Advances in software/hardware research and development will continue to influence the entire planet. No longer are the results of these efforts localized. Asimov explains:

> What I foresee is a society in intense creative ferment, people reaching out to others, new thoughts arising and spreading at a speed never before imagined, change and variety filling the planet (to say nothing of the smaller, artificial worlds that will be constructed in space). It will be a new world that will look back at earlier centuries as having been only half alive. (p. 59)

Communication Technology and Communication Systems: Future Growth and Development

Advances in communication technology and the development of new and unique applications of communication systems will change the home, education of children and adults, training and retraining in business and industry, business services, industrial products, and the manner in which governments evolve relationships (in peace-time or warfare modes).

The access to information via sophisticated communication networks will enhance existing private and public sector functions. There are an abundance of predictable evolutions and unpredictable innovations which will cause the creation of new businesses and services. All will impact the evolving technology education curriculum as educators seek new and varied ways to reflect the concepts, processes, systems, and impacts encompassed or influenced by communication technologies. Presented in this section is a small sampling of technologies and applications which will find their way into the future lectures and discussions, activities, and explorations of children studying about the expanded capabilities of communication technology.

Linking Information Employees and Technology

Futurist David Snyder (1987) indicated that at the beginning of the 1980's 2.7 percent of all American workers were in agriculture, by comparison to the dominant sector of our economy, information work, which employed 52 1/2 percent of all workers in 1987. Figure 10.1 presents the four major sectors of the U.S. labor force for a period of 1860 through 1995.

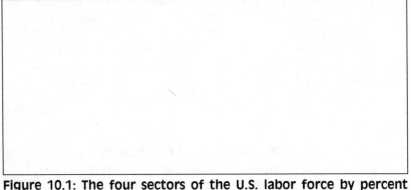

Figure 10.1: The four sectors of the U.S. labor force by percent 1860-1995.

Educators are information workers. With the exception of the maintenance people, cooks, and school bus drivers, all of the people in education are information workers. Snyder contended that "the second largest industry in America - both in terms of employment and expenditures - is education" (p. 3).

Snyder (1987a) reported that in government, about half of all workers are information workers. "That is to say, the value added by what they do comes from their handling of information: their analysis, application, consolidation, distribution of information to make better decisions" (p. 3). People employed in management are also information workers. One quarter of the employees in the three largest auto makers are in management.

Snyder contended that information employees are the "least capitalized." In the early 1980's the capitalization rate per employee was estimated at $8,500.00 per employee, i.e. the amount of money spent on each information employee by business and industry for the technology being utilized by them in their work. With a personal computer costing approximately $2,000.00 one can readily see that expenditures have been made on other items than just the end user devices (a personal computer). Snyder (1987b) referred to the information infrastructure as "the infostructure: millions of miles of fiber-optic cable, communication dishes and communication satellites, networks, data bases, software" (p. 6).

Once the investment of thousands of dollars per information employee are made on information related technologies, the end user devices such as the personal computer will be even more powerful to use. The average person and information worker will be able to access a powerful amount of information and be able to perform very complex interactive tasks. The major assets of large industrial enterprises in the future will not be the physical plant or the equipment contained therein, but "it will be the data bases, the software, the expert systems. Data networks will be the fabric upon which value-added will move all over the world" (Snyder, 1987b, p. 6).

According to Brophy (1987), recent breakthroughs are sharpening the focus and potential of information technologies. Businesses now look to concentrate on large-scale integration or "enterprise communications" (p. 88). The term "enterprise communications" refers to using technology to improve communications among knowledge workers (information employees), professionals whose creativity and decision-making capabilities are dependent on multiple sources or extensive data banks of information. Communication technology must be able to facilitate the sharing of information, peer-to-peer, across an entire organization in order to ensure effective decision making. The time value of information is also increasing, and will affect the way decisions are made.

Multimedia Technologies

"Education must anticipate the future" maintained Snyder (1987c, p. 91). "Employers faced with huge increases in their in-house training costs, will be required to develop productivity-enhancing teaching technologies" (p. 92). The reality is that the work force will be required to change careers or be substantially retrained to utilize new information technologies.

The public schools continue to be confronted by the public and government demands for improved education with limited financial and human resources. Public education will also be forced to adopt a wide range of innovative educational delivery arrangements claimed Snyder (1987c). These arrangements will apply multimedia technologies using communication networks to enhance training and education.

Instructional and presentation delivery technologies have advanced rapidly through microcomputer integration and networking capabilities as well as the development of authoring and expert systems software. Research continues to determine how advanced software systems and multi-media technologies may be effectively utilized within the education and training environment.

Advanced technology classrooms (Stickrod, 1989, Horowitz, 1988, and Vadas, 1988) employ multi-media and hyper-media applications with the potential of improving the teaching and learning environment. IBM's "Advanced Technology Classroom" concept like Apple's "Hypermedia Laboratories" integrate text, graphics, animation, video, CD-based image storage and full audio capabilities in an interactive mode between the computer system, the instructor and the student. The IBM "Advanced Technology Classroom" (IBM, 1989) uses a high quality audio/visual system capable of displaying digitized images, generating high resolution computer graphics, and features an electronic blackboard. Classroom productivity is reportedly increased through a reduction of instructor dependency, enhanced consistency, stimulated learning processes, and improved retention (through increased interactivity).

According to Davis, Sasnett, and Hodges (1989), a research and development program at MIT sponsored primarily by DEC and IBM explored similar multi-media applications. These researchers were able to reduce the time and skills needed by faculty to produce interactive multi-media software for educational purposes by developing and field testing a multi-media workstation. Authoring and expert systems software enable the user via prompts to create consistent, effective, and systematic instruction. Media events can be sequenced for presentations and a variety of outputs include: reports, graphics, development of specifications, and disks for use in the classroom (ATCAP, 1989). Yencharis (1989) reported that "integrated image technologies based on open system standards for research were highlighted in last year's presentation by a select committee sponsored by the National Science Foundation" (p. 72). He contended that end users will begin to utilize such high performance technologies as tools rather than scientific curiosities.

Advanced technology classrooms and laboratories are the future instructional environment. They employ multi-media technologies for the purpose of providing improved instructional delivery and enhanced learning. The application and utilization of this environment may make the teaching and learning of rapidly changing communication technology and business/industry advances more effective.

Artificial Intelligence and Neural Networks

According to a recent article in the Science and Technology section of *The Economist* (1990), Dr. Hans Moravec in his recent book, *Mind Children*, describes a future "in which computers will match all the mental abilities and quirks of people" (p. 89). Moravec and other visionaries of artificial intelligence believe this will happen by about the year 2030. It borderlines on science fiction and there are many skeptics.

Philosophers such as Dr. John Searle, who published a paper in 1980 presenting his "Chinese-Room" argument, have attempted to prove that early artificial intelligence researchers were confused about the ability to have computers think and reason in the same manner as humans. To make his point, Searle imagined himself as a computer sitting in a room with two windows. Through one window came pieces of paper (input) with questions written in Chinese. It was his job to process the information using a rule book for Chinese writing and pass through the second window (output) the right answers to the questions. He matched the patterns in the rule book to the patterns presented in the questions and generated the answers using the same rules. In effect, he was running a program that gives correct answers to Chinese even though he did not personally understand Chinese. The "program" mimiced the understanding of Chinese and could not do anything more. Thus, Searle believed that to program a computer to perform such tasks is not to make artificial minds but to manipulate symbols according to rules.

The "new" artificial intelligence researchers, called "connectionists" believe that the way to make artificial minds is not by writing complex programs for computers but to build "brain-like machines" that can program themselves. They believe that a computer with a large number of simple processors, each connected to many others and performing many computations at the same time can learn to "weaken or strengthen the connections between processors, and thus in effect program itself to think" (*The Economist*, 1990, p. 89). Effectively what occurs is that the computer simulates the billions of neurons which each human has in their brain and behaves in a similar fashion to the neurons in the brain. These computer connections or creations are called neural networks.

Drs. Patricia and Paul Churchland, philosophers at the University of California at San Diego, believe that neural networks can answer the "Chinese-Room" argument posed by Dr. Searle. They contend that through the use of parallel processors neural networks are much more similar to the human brain than traditional computers are, "so it is reasonable to suppose that once they become sophisticated enough, they will think" (*The Economist*, 1990, p. 89). Since these machines will use massive parallel processors to perform the "neural networking" the argument of whether or not the computer can perform human reasoning and thinking continues.

Dr. Searle contended that humans are different from computers because the computations which occur in the human brain have different causes and effects than those which occur in the computer. "It is because of the way people interact with the world that the words they use have meanings which they can understand and ponder" (*The Economist*, 1990, p. 89).

Satellite Technology and Service Bureaus

GTE Spacenet Corporation, a provider of business communications services using the latest satellite technology, reported that while large industries are using satellite transmission there has been slow growth and a reluctance among small companies to make the large capital investments in using the technology because of its rapid evolution. According to Gold and Pierson (1987) of GTE, satellite-based data transmission networks could streamline operations.

Several years ago, the Gannett company decided to send its newspaper, *USA Today*, to print via satellite. This system allowed the paper to be printed at numerous sites, cutting the cost of printing and distribution. Today, the *USA Today* network transmits to more than 30 printing plants at a data rate of about 150 kilobits/second. Despite the size and complexity of this network, reported Gold and Pierson (1987, p. 64), no issue of the newspaper have ever missed delivery due to a satellite problem. This huge and expensive undertaking legitimized the use of satellites for the transmission of facsimile color (photographs and graphics) and text information. Other similar firms which use satellite networks include The New York Times Company and Dow Jones (*The Wall Street Journal*).

The large newspaper publishers now rely on satellite networks to conduct daily business operations. GTE Spacenet created an automated satellite communications system to attract smaller companies who could not commit themselves to long term contracts due to the high cost of the multi-year contracts, not enough work to justify the expense, or no desire to be locked into a transmission network at the time. What was created was a satellite transmission "service bureau" designed to satisfy a wide range of image and text transmission requirements for business and industry applications. Customers send and receive digitized images and/or text at various data rates and pay only for the satellite time they actually use.

The concept of "service bureaus" are extending to other areas within communication technology. The copy center which used to perform the task of making multiple electrostatic copies from original black and white text copy now has a host of interconnected (networked) devices for the purpose of serving the customers imaging needs. The customer may bring in their computer disk from home or office with a document to be output through a high quality laser printer or a photograph may be scanned via a flat-bed unit and the data placed onto disk for the customer's use in a newsletter or brochure. Computer modem links are also utilized to telecommunicate data or images between the customer and the service bureau. What the company now offers the customer are services which would be too expensive for the customer to afford in their home or small business. Fees are charged based on the type of data input or output processed and the expense of operating the device. Color input and output are the two major growth areas where service bureaus will extend themselves in the near future.

High Definition Television

High definition television (HDTV) is rapidly becoming a technological imperative. Even though there is not a perceived human or societal need for HDTV, the fact that HDTV is on the technological horizon is inevitable. Winner asks, "What is so good on television that we need a 60-inch, theater-quality screen with digital stereophonic sound blaring at us?" (1989, p. 20). What occurs with high definition television is the replacement of the 525 horizontal lines in current receivers with 1,000 to 1,250 lines. The arguments for further research and development in this area are being supported by recent high-tech promotions. According to Winner (1989), advocates of HDTV point out that the Japanese and European manufacturers are rapidly developing HDTV systems.

HDTV encompasses an entire array of related technologies. For business, industry, and the consumer, the HDTV market includes: HDTV receivers, cameras, video recorders, and the broadcast and cable equipment that accompany them. The next generation of warfare electronics will require the use of high quality visual displays associated with HDTV. The government and military users desire the assurance that producers can supply the equipment they will require to support advanced weapons technology. Winner (1989) reported that the Defense Advanced Research Projects Agency (DARPA) recently budgeted $30 million to support research and development on improved television.

The Technology of Stealth

The ultimate in "high technology" advances have been integrated by companies contracted by governments throughout the world in the design and manufacture of warfare technology. The technology of stealth is just one example of a host of communication technologies being integrated to create systems which defy human senses and traditional warfare sensing and detection devices.

Goldberg (1989) explained that stealth is often equated with making an object less visible to radar. "Although this is an important consideration, designers must try to minimize other signatures, or sets of identifying traits, as well" (p. 35). In addition to the radar "signature" or profile which a weapon or vehicle has, it also gives of an "infrared, an electro-optical, an acoustic, and an eletromagnetic signature" (p. 35) which can be picked up by electronic sensors or human eyes and ears. These signatures are usually detected by some form of communication system designed to specifically intercept the signals or emissions of each type of signature.

The anti-radar design goal for stealth weapons and vehicles is to create surfaces which are contoured and are made of highly absorbent materials. Researchers at Carnegie-Mellon in 1987 discovered lightweight substances (Schiff base salts) which absorb a wide range of radar frequencies. The Air Force Advanced Technology Fighter (ATF), a stealth plane, is scheduled for production in the mid-1990's. It is expected to reflect 99 percent less radar than a normal fighter or about as much as a pigeon, (Goldberg, 1989). The infrared (or heat) signatures are more difficult to eliminate. Goldberg indicated that missiles which use infrared sensors "have downed more combat planes this decade than any other weapon" (p. 36). Infrared sensors are less detectable than radar because the systems are passive, emitting no signals.

"Guidance and tracking systems based on lasers or TV cameras" are becoming more common described Goldberg (1989, p. 36). Hiding an aircraft from such systems as are on air-to-surface missiles and laser guidance for surface-to-air missiles is basically the same as hiding the plane from the human eye. Light enables the aircraft to be visible and as such designers are trying to make the planes blend better with their surroundings. One concept is called "active camouflage." This technique causes the plane's surface to shift constantly to match the background. Acoustic, or noise, reduction is a major problem that is not easily solved by exterior design and improved communication systems engineering. Moving parts are redesigned to create more efficient engines with lower noise emissions.

Emissions from on-board systems such as communications, radar, and avionics cause electromagnetic signatures. Stealth designers are trying to make communications harder to intercept. The application of laser communications, based on finely focused beams, provide high-speed data transmissions which are undetectable. Goldberg (1989) indicated that McDonnel Douglas is under contract to produce a prototype laser that will transmit 100 megabits of data per minute and thus facilitate this process.

Communication Technology in Technology Education

The on-going dilemma for technology educators at all levels will be what to emphasize in courses within the curriculum to provide the comprehensive study of communication technology. The future trends in communication technology and the further development of the "information age" may lead technology educators to expand further the study of communication systems with a conscious focus on the creation, utilization/processing, and access/storage of "information". "A system is a group of components working together or influencing each other - that is, communicating with each other in some way" contended Bugliarello (1989, p. 31). Accordingly, "all systems, both natural and human-made, are internally coordinated by processes that convey information."

Johnson (1989) in *Technology, the Report of the Project 2061 Phase I Technology Panel*, maintained:

> To participate fully in the information age, young adults should understand - at least conceptually - the technologies

that are behind modern communications. Further, they should be aware of the ideas, risks, and benefits of information management that are made possible by advancing communications technology. (p. 23)

As Isaac Asimov indicated, the education of the "technochild" will require different approaches and creative planning, perhaps unique strategies never before explored by technology educators.

There are many questions which must be asked and require immediate attention as the study of communication technology in technology education replaces the traditional efforts of industrial education to teach drafting, graphic arts, electronics, photography, and computers, for example, independently.

Ten "big" questions to consider, conceptualize, and act on:

1. When will the study of communication technology extend across all grade levels in our schools?

2. Will students in communication technology courses study the services and functions performed with communication technologies (devices and networks) and will the communication systems of business and industry (which use and apply many technologies) be included?

3. Will activities center around the concepts, processes, and outcomes of applying communication devices/systems to solving problems which face business/industry and society?

4. Will an emphasis be placed on the personal, societal, environmental (etc.) impacts of communication systems in our world and will technology education teachers facilitate the identification and exploration of global issues and concerns?

5. Will the study of communication technology in technology education be all inclusive? Will all communication technologies (mechanical, optical, audio, visual, electrical, biological, etc.) be "fair game"?

6. How well will the facilities, equipment, and supplies required to teach communication technology be supported by administrators through school budgets or via donations from business/industry?

7. How and where will the classroom teachers be prepared to develop/select new curriculum and course materials, understand and use new technologies, and deliver a future oriented program?

8. How will issues of accreditation, assessment and accountability, educational reform, standards, and value-added education change the future of technology education?

9. Are the technology education teachers of today ready to make the transitions needed for public education in the future to include technology education taught by technology teachers (versus science or social studies teachers OR with science, mathematics and social studies teachers, for example)?

10. Who will make the decisions and provide the direction?

For some educators these questions concerning the study of communication technology pose exciting new challenges and a bright future in the classroom. For other educators the conversion of curriculum is perceived as an unnecessary or impossible task which may challenge an established philosophy of industrial education and as such cause conflict. This conflict may be due to years of teaching the same courses (successfully or otherwise), the prospect of learning new information/devices/approaches, lack of support or too much support for change from the school administration, or a host of other factors.

Curricular change eventually influences a series events to occur in the educational setting. The most positive of which is the effect which an exciting and relevant technology curriculum will have on the students (technochildren). The most important reason for change is the student and the opportunities which must be provided to them. Educators can not lose sight of the goal to prepare students to function as productive citizens in a technologically-based society. All too often the educational goals are sacrificed for the personal interests and "comfort level" of the teacher. Often teachers will teach what they were taught and in the same manner as they were taught. Luckily, that pattern from the past is changing. Preparing children for the future requires everyone to make a commitment to change, that's not only a commitment to students but ultimately it's a commitment to society.

Where Are We and Where Are We Going?

The teaching of communication in technology education has evolved from a progression of curriculum developments as were discussed in Chapter 3. No longer does technology education need to justify or rationalize communication technology as a viable area for study. Continued implementation at all levels is expected.

Three chapters in this Yearbook (Chapters 4, 5, and 6) were dedicated to provide an orientation to and models for the teaching of communication technology at all levels within the curriculum. Each author presented unique and varied approaches which teachers can adapt and adopt for their school's program. All rely on the presentation of communication systems (as described in Chapter 1), the relationship to business and industry trends (Chapters 2 and 10), and creating the teaching/learning environment where activities will be a dynamic experience for students (Chapters 7, 8, and 9).

The constants which are essential to the planning of future curriculum rest with the goals of technology education itself. The study of communication systems must be supportive of the overall effort to study the "creation, utilization, and behavior of adaptive systems in relation to humans, their societies, and the life-giving and life-sustaining environment" (ITEA, 1988, p. 10). Technology education programs have deliberate areas of emphasis and focus depending upon the grade level. The teaching of communication must be coordinated with these efforts.

At the elementary level the focus is on technological awareness with an emphasis on "how people create and control their environment" (ITEA, 1988, p. 17). The elementary program is designed to integrate through interdisciplinary activities other subjects (science, mathematics, etc.). Students work with "tools, materials, and technical concepts and processes" (p. 17).

As a student progresses to the middle school level the focus turns to the exploration of technology. Activities center on contemporary technologies and the processes associated with them. Career awareness and exploration is included and students "study and analyze the materials, products, processes, problems, uses, developments, and contributions of these career related fields" (ITEA, 1988, p. 18). The structure of organizations and management in business and industry is introduced at the middle school level. In addition, students "research, plan, design, construct, and evaluate problems and projects" (ITEA, p. 18) related to the technologies being studied. "Technology Education activities provide the student at this level with an endless amount of opportunities to create and problem solve. These opportunities are similar to those which will be encountered in their technological future" (ITEA, 1988, p. 18).

High school level technology education programs enable students to apply scientific and mathematical principles to the study of technological systems. Students are provided with the framework for making career and educational decisions concerning their future. They gain an "in-depth understanding and appreciation for technology in our society and culture," they "develop basic skills in the proper use of tools, machines, materials, and processes," and "solve problems" relating to the processes and products of industry and technology.

To highlight these goals one can look back to the information presented by the American Industrial Arts Association in the publication, *Technology Education: A Perspective on Implementation* (AIAA, 1985). The curriculum structure for technology education presented in that document provides goals which continue to support the future direction of technology education and the teaching of communication in technology education. See Figure 10-2.

Level:	Goal:
K-6	Technological Awareness
6-9	Orientation and Exploration
9-12	Preparation in Technology

Figure 10-2. Curriculum structure for technology education (Adapted from *Technology Education: A Perspective on Implementation*, AIAA, 1985, p. 25-26.).

The corresponding communication courses in technology education to the grade levels and goals indicated in Figure 10-2 are provided in Figure 10-3.

Level:	Communication Courses/Emphasis:
K-6	Interdisciplinary (Courses creating an awareness of communication technology.)
6-7	Introduction to Technological Systems (Provide an orientation and exploration of major technological systems.)
8-9	Communication Systems (Provide an orientation and exploration of major communication systems.)
9-12	Communication Systems (Specific and significant communication systems such as audio, video, graphic, visual, electronic, media, telecommunication, or other appropriate descriptors may be broken out into separate courses depending on the school program and size.)

Figure 10-3. Communication Courses in Technology Education.

191

Zuga (1989) in her presentation of curriculum planning in technology education explained:

How we determine the content of the curriculum in technology education will influence students' experiences in the classroom. If we select a series of social problems, a list of technical processes, a structure of critical thinking and problem solving skills, a taxonomy of concepts of technology, or allow students to select technology-related problems which are significant to them, then the curriculum as a plan and as taught will appear to be different in each case. This difference will also appear in the way in which we analyze technology for the purpose of creating curriculum. (p. 53)

Some examples of future oriented communication studies are briefly included in this section to reinforce the point that adapting, adopting, and implementing new approaches within the technology education framework is essential. Thode (1989) described "Technology Education in the Elementary School" contending:

Technology-related information should be presented to students at an early age. Developing an awareness of the effects of technology today and in the future, as well as developing the ability to adapt to changes brought about by technological advancements are important concepts to explore. (p. 12)

Children begin school already aware of many communication technologies. Supporting their continued growth and understanding of the role which these systems and devices have on their lives is essentially where the elementary program begins. The MESH program in Idaho integrates "Multimedia, Environmental, Sciences and Humanities" to introduce technology concepts to elementary children "in a hands-on environment" (Thode, p. 13). The integration of technology studies with other subjects in an interdisciplinary approach has increased program successes not only in Idaho but in similar elementary technology programs in other states.

According to Thode (1989), in the MESH program "the communications area integrates easily with the regular classroom curricula involving science, math, geography, language arts and reading" (p. 14). Activities explore communication systems via experiments in photography, sound and video presentations, electronics principles, satellite communications, and the utilization of modems to access databases.

Mission 21, supported by a training grant from the National Aeronautics & Space Administration (NASA), "was designed to stimulate student interest in the study of science, mathematics, and technology in an effort to ensure their active participation in our increasingly technological society" (Brusic et al, 1988, p. 23). Within this model program the students participate at the third through sixth grade level in problem-solving and creative thinking activities. The fifth and sixth grade themes include communication, space colonization, inventions, and energy and matter.

In "A Technology Education Model for Ohio," Savage (1990) presented a technology systems model and models for technology education at the primary, middle school and secondary grades. He defined communication technology systems in the following manner:

> These systems reflect technology that involves the use of devices or methods to collect, process, store, or deliver communication using electronic, graphic, photographic, and/or mechanical means. (p. 9)

The Ohio Model supports the work of Hendricks and Sterry (1987) (see also Chapter 6). Savage provides a systems model which depicts how communication technology systems focus on "the processes and techniques of encoding, transmitting, receiving, storing, retrieving, and decoding graphic and electronic messages" (1990, p. 11).

Swyt (1987) presented technology curriculum organizers "designed to capture the entirety of all technologies, past, present and future" (p. 7). Swyt explained that "technology must be taught at every level of our educational system" (p. 7.). Within his presentation he described four organizers: physical, material, information, and bio. "Information" as one content organizer for the study of technology included the study of data, information and knowledge via such subcategories as: computers, expert systems/AI, optical fibers, and database systems.

Summary

As technology educators we are challenged by the future, challenged by changing technology and curriculum orientations. The methods we employ to deliver education to the youth of today and tomorrow must be dynamic. We are required to have boundless vitality and energy. The personal motivation as a teacher to have students succeed in a technological world is essential to the success of technology education. The extent to which communication technology and communication systems are taught throughout the K-12 and college/university curriculum is dependent upon commitment and action. This Yearbook challenges all technology educators to make the commitment and take action toward effective and quality instruction and learning activities in communication. Communication technologies are the very essence of the "information age" and the progress ofall societies will involve the interplay which new inventions and innovations have with evolving systems and networks.

References

Advanced technology classroom authoring program (ATCAP). (1989). Thornwood, NY: International Business Machines.

American Industrial Arts Association (AIAA). (1985). *Technology education: A perspective on implementation.* Reston, VA: AIAA

Asimov, I. (1989). Future fantastic. *Personal Computing Sourcebook*, pp. 56-59.

Brophy, J. T. (1987, September). Linking knowledge workers and information technology. *The Office*, p. 88, 90, 92.

Brusic, S. A., Dunlap, D. D., Dugger, W. E., & LaPorte, J. E. (1988, December). Launching technology education into elementary classrooms. *The Technology Teacher, 48*(3), 23-25.

Bugliarello, G. (1989). *Physical and information sciences and engineering.* Washington, DC: American Association for the Advancement of Science.

Davis, B., Sasnett, R., & Hodges, M. (1989, July/August). Educational multimedia at MIT. *Advanced Imaging*, 4(7), 32, 34-35.

Goldberg, J. H. (1989, May/June). The technology of stealth. *Technology Review*, 92(4), pp. 33-40.

Gold, M., & Pierson, J. (1987, October). Satellite technology to impact color houses/graphic arts firms. *Graphic Arts Monthly*, pp. 64, 68, 72.

Hendricks, R. W. & Sterry, L. F. (1987). *Communication technology.* Menomonie, WI: T & E Publications.

Horowitz, H. M. (1988). Student response systems: Interactivity in a classroom environment. Paper presented at the meeting of the Society for Applied Learning Technology.

International Business Machines (IBM). (1989). *Advanced technology classroom.* Thornwood, NY: IBM.

International Technology Education Association (ITEA). (1988). *Technology a national imperative.* Reston, VA: ITEA.

Johnson, J. R. (1989). *Technology.* Washington, DC: American Association for the Advancement of Science.

Savage, E. (1990). A technology education model for Ohio. *The Technology Teacher.* 49(5), 8-12.

Snyder, D. (1987, July). Inevitable forces for change. *Insight*, 4(7), pp. 1-7.

Snyder, D. (1987, August). Inevitable forces for change. *Insight*, 4(8), pp. 1-6.

Snyder, D. P. (1987). Learning for life in revolutionary times: Imperatives for American educators in a decade of techno-economic change. *Journal of Studies in Technical Careers, 9*(2), 91-101.

Staff. (1990, January 27). Artificial intelligence or maybe not. *The Economist*, p. 89.

Stickrod, R. (1989, April). Hypermedia: More than the next buzzword. *Computer Graphics World*, 4(4), 53.

Swyt, D. A. (1987, September/October). An agenda for progress in technology education. *The Technology Teacher*, 47(1), 3-8.

Thode, T. (1989, September/October). Technology education in the elementary school. *The Technology Teacher*, 49(1), 12-15.

Vadas, J. E. (1988). Interactive videodisc for management training in a classroom environment. Paper presented at the meeting of the Society for Applied Learning Technology.

Winner, L. (1989, May/June). Who needs HDTV? *Technology Review, 92*(4), p. 20.

Yencharis, L. R. (1989, April). That imaging/graphics marriage: Long engagement or early divorce. *Advanced Imaging*, 4(4), 18, 20, 22, & 72.

Zuga, K. F. (1989). Relating technology education goals to curriculum planning. *Journal of Technology Education, 1*(1), 34-58.

Index

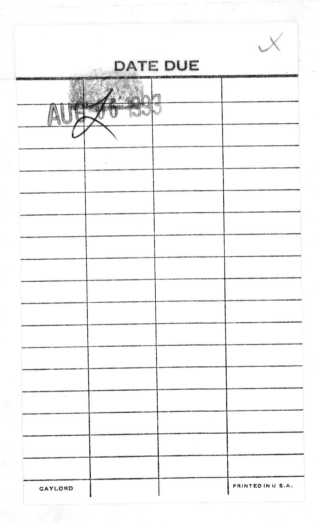